Total health is a 3-pa
... it's time to connect

Spirit, Soul, & B

DR. JOHNNETT THATCHER, DC

FOREWORD *by* BENI JOHNSON

TABLE OF CONTENTS

FOREWORD

Many years ago, I started on my journey to wholeness. It began with the healing of my soul and spirit and continued, finally, to my physical health. I've often wondered why I waited until the medical doctor told me, "You know you're going to have to do something about that hyper-tension?" I had watched a family member go down that road and didn't like what I saw. So, I decided to go find out how I could heal and walk in health without all the medications and all the side effects from those medications. I read books, did research on the Internet, and began realizing that there was in fact other ways to heal. Now, don't get me wrong. It's not that I'm against medication when needed, but I personally decided that that would not be my first choice.

I live a very busy life, and I travel for a lot of that busy life. If you travel, you know that just getting on a plane is enough to put stress in your body. I remember coming back from one international trip and I was exhausted. I had flown 5 international trips in 5 months. I had just recovered from adrenal fatigue issues and thought I would try to increase my travel again. By the time I was flying home from this 5th trip, I leaned over to my assistant and said, "This isn't going to work." I could feel my body going down that same, exhausted, worn-out trial. Either something had to change or I had to find a way to get this lifestyle to work.

Then, I ran into Dr. Johnnett. I had been wanting to get my blood work done for some time just to see what was going on. Someone recommended that I meet Dr. Johnnett. We met, talked, and the journey back to a healthy, livable lifestyle began. I am very thankful for Dr. Johnnett's wisdom and knowledge. Not only is she

wealthy in body health but also health for the whole person—spirit, soul and body. We are, after all, a triune being and in order to live in health we have to go after total health in all three areas.

Now, I know that many who I have talked to have told me, "The health world is so confusing; I don't know where to start." I get that. It can be. That's why its important to find those who know their field well. In Dr. Johnnett's book, you will find a wealth of information that can help you navigate through the maze of total body health.

I am so thankful to have met, and continue to be under the care of, a knowledgeable woman such as Dr. Johnnett. Not only is she my care provider but she is also a good friend. She is full of life, and she makes you feel like you can do this. We can be healthy and well.

Thank you Johnnett for writing this timely book.

Beni Johnson
Redding, California
Author of *Healthy and Free, 40 Days to Wholeness* and *The Happy Intercessor*

INTRODUCTION

There was a seed who wondered as it sat amidst its community thinking, "When will I become all that I was made for? I am tired and dry and have been sitting here for so long with so many others who are also doing nothing it seems." The tiny seed knew that in order to grow it needed to be immersed in the dirt, covered in darkness while receiving nutrients. It needed to engage in the struggle to reach the light in order to produce the life of abundance for which it knew it was destined. As it pondered its destiny, a hand reached down and picked up seed and threw it to the ground. The appointed time had come! And thus, the life process began…

I love the way the Lord designed the process of life. He could have chosen to create us as grown adults, free from the journey of growth and process. He could have brought us into this world with all the knowledge that we would need to be able to adequately survive. However, He decided to be the God of process. The God who created babies. You see, God loves the journey of life. He loves watching learn how to sit up, crawl, walk, and run. Every part of the journey has value to Him. When we are children first learning to crawl, he doesn't condemn us up for not immediately trying to walk. Each failed attempt, tumble, and success brings immeasurable joy to his heart.

The seed in the story above represents our life and it carries life! Each of our lives carries destiny that is only released through divinely ordered timing and process. That process begins with a timely burial of the seed in dirt and darkness. In that unique and seemingly uninviting environment, the seed requires necessities such as water and moisture to rehydrate the dried seed and allow it to access its internal reservoir of nutritional resources. Once optimal moisture has been absorbed, the seed activates enzymes from within to provoke the growing embryo to breakthrough its outer shell, which then allows the embryo to come forth and form roots. Those roots push and grow downwards in order to stabilize and position the seedling while simultaneously allowing the buried seed itself to be pushed upward to break through the earth toward the light! As nutrients and light continue to bathe the seedling, it accelerates its growth process to maturity; producing seed for abundant harvest and return to seed to repeat the life cycle again for generations to come.

Each of our lives mirror this parable and the life journey of a seed. As a practitioner, I have seen this played out beautifully and powerfully in the lives of many of those whom I have been entrusted to treat. My heart in writing this book is to invite you on a journey. There will be breakthroughs and set backs, paths clearly marked and paths that seem unending. But I encourage you to not lose hope. Keep your eye on the destination, which is total health and wholeness in Jesus. Remember that not a single step goes unnoticed. After all, seed by seed and row by row, that's how you make a garden grow….

This book is titled *Well, Well, Well* for a number of reasons. First, we all want to be well. Secondly, we need to take a look at where our "wellness" comes from. And thirdly, our definition and experience of wellness needs, like a seed, to grow and produce fruit in our lives! All of these reasons are why I wanted to write this book because I want to propose to you a new model of health that will take our "wellness" to a much higher level.

Let's begin with the body because that is each of our most obvious focal point. I've found that pain is often humanity's highest motivating factor. We've all heard it said, "If it's not broken, don't fix it!" Yet that is a false approach to health! However, it does form the foundation for the traditional Western medical system, which is practically "when it hurts or breaks we work to fix what is broken.[1] "In translation, the western medical system is more symptoms driven.

I believe with all my heart that there is a better model available that we can integrate to bring a higher level of life and health to our community and ourselves. I offer it as a new model but it actually has ancient roots, which can be found in God's Word. I just want to clarify that as a healthcare professional, it is an honor to be counted among the medical community in that medicine has come so far and brings so much healing to problems that in centuries past had no

---

1 Our medical model addresses the body and rarely integrates any other aspect of our being when seeking solutions to our physical ailments. If we take a quick overview of the current medical model we see several things. First, the model we are most familiar with is the current western Medical Model known as Allopathic medicine which includes MDs, DOs, Nurses, Pharmacists, Radiologists and countless others. It concerns a system in which medical doctors and other healthcare professionals (such as nurses, pharmacists, and therapists) treat symptoms and diseases using drugs, radiation, or surgery. It does so often through specialties such as Cardiovascular, Urology, Obstetrics, Gynecology, Neurology, Gastroenterology,

Eyes, Ears, Nose, and Throat, Pulmonary, Endocrinology and Oncology to name a few.

There is another vein of medicine called functional medicine that looks to find the root cause or mechanism involved with any loss of function, which ultimately reveals why a set of symptoms is there in the first place, or why the patient has a particular disease label. Functional Medicine is an integrative, science-based healthcare approach that treats illness and promotes wellness by focusing on the bio-chemically unique aspects of each patient, and then individually tailoring interventions to restore physiological, psychological, and structural balance. The practitioners in this field include Alternative MDs, DOs, Chiropractors, Naturopathic Doctor, Homeopathy.

These two streams typically operate independent from and alternative to each other in practice. I am so very thankful for each and every discipline within both sides of the medical profession and recognize the need for each of them.

remedy. That being said, I offer this material in the hopes to build a bridge for all aspects of medicine and healers . My goal is to take a serious look at integrating every level of medicine, not just in the body, but also in the realms of the soul (mind, will, and emotions) and spirit. For we are spirit, we have a soul, and we live in a body.

In the Bible, we read in I Thessalonians 5:23, "Now may the God of peace Himself sanctify you entirely; and may your spirit and soul and body be preserved complete, without blame at the coming of our Lord Jesus Christ."[2] This is a foundational scripture for what I propose because it makes it clear that from God's perspective we are a three part (body, soul, and spirit) whole individual and each part is of value to God!

I have found that in order to restore and maintain wellness in an individual, it is imperative to focus on each patient individually and to bring into practice an emerging medicine that addresses the spirit, soul and body. In 3 John 2 we read, "Beloved I wish above all things, that you would prosper and be in *health,* even as your *soul* prospers."[3] This truth is the foundation for my practice. We must begin to unlock and address the individual's true and whole self, which is the body, soul, and spirit. The primacy of this foundational principle will unfold as we progress.

Beginning with the body, it is important that we look at the root causes of all symptoms and diseases. Statistically, it is estimated that over 80% of patients fall in the flow of conventional medicine. Conventional medicine is great for short-term care for the individual but it fails to solve the root cause of the problem. The other 20% of patients go straight into functional medicine and begin to discover and unlock wellness from within their own bodies. I say "bravo!" to both path! However, I can't help but wonder much more

2 New International Version
3 King James Version, emphasis added

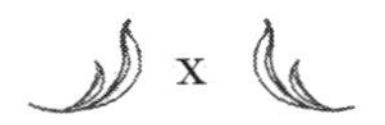

powerful the healthcare system would be if we could stop arguing about our differences and embrace the strengths of each sector and specialty. That can only happen if we recognize the fundamental truth that we stand and serve to assist the patient in achieving a symptom-free life coupled with the ability to pull out the root of the disease that ails them.

Our society has a desire to receive their health at the same lightning speed we expect of our Internet connections. Unfortunately, that typically is delivered in the form of a pill. Pharmaceuticals have risen to an addictive level for a variety of reasons, but mostly because they offer a quick and simple solution to bigger problems. "Fast" is not necessarily a solution in all circumstances. Instead, we must educate people on how to adapt to a lifestyle change. We as healthcare practitioners need to approach patients in the way our bodies are designed which is the spirit, soul, and body.

In most medical offices, when a patient enters a clinic they have to fill out an in depth history form. This gives the doctor a glimpse into their past, present and potentially even their future. Within the medical history, the patient completes what we call a review of symptoms. This section reviews each system of the body. A few examples would be their digestive system, heart health, and blood sugar levels. In addition, we review family history, as well as social history. All of these items help the practitioner to see which steps to take in facilitating diagnostic tests in order to aid in the diagnosis and treatment protocols for the illnesses presented. Both conventional and functional medicines utilize these procedures where both strategies are integrated to bring the best results for the patient.

However, this is not the end of history taking. In fact, let me take you (figuratively!) to our clinic in Indiana where we implemented one of our Body, Soul and Spirit History and Patient Intake. In our practice, we discovered that patients have not always sustained their healing. As we began to take histories of their soul and spirit health, we were able to see reoccurring patterns and correlations with their sickness and emotions. The research shows in overwhelming statistics that our thought life will direct us down a road of either life or death. Our thoughts and emotions derive from our soul and spirit and if we bring health to those areas, then our physical healing will remain.

Indeed, every thought you have has either a positive pathway of life or a negative pathway to death! Life experiences play a key role in our thought life. My husband and I have seen first hand the miracles that come forth in teaching and coaching patients through a curriculum we have incorporated in our practice called "Pathways to Wholeness." In that curriculum, we learn that if the fruit of our thought life is love, joy, peace, patience, kindness, goodness, faithfulness, gentleness, and self-control, then healing comes. If the fruit of our thought life is bitterness (to self or to others) unforgiveness, resentment, retaliation, anger, wrath, hatred, violence, murder, accusation (throwing or receiving), envy, jealousy, rejection (to self or to others), addiction, self-focus, fear (anxiety/ stress), and traumas, than those bring death. We have seen first-hand that when patients redirect their thought life to pathways of life, life comes! When every thought is held captive, they come out of their captivity! The destructive cycles must be turned off and reset to the cycles of life!

Returning to our seed parable, life is a repetitive process much like the growth and harvest cycle of gardening or farming. So it is with our health that certain practices must be repeated over and over again in our attempt to capture and maintain our health in all the dimensions of our being. Let's explore what that looks like as we make this journey together.

Chapter 1

AGAIN AND AGAIN

Through the course of my practice, I spent many days and nights asking the Lord for insight when it came to total body healing. I knew that since God created us in three parts (body, soul, and spirit) that we could never be fully healed without being fully connected to the presence and goodness of God. I would see people do everything they could to fight sickness and disease in the physical aspect by taking supplements and eating well, but something was still off. Eventually, they would find themselves either back in the same predicament or facing a completely new and alarming challenge with their health. I knew that since we are made of a body, a soul, and spirit that there had to be a way to combine and bring healing to our entire being. Eventually, the Lord began speaking to me through words.

Restore
Rebuild
Refresh

What stood out to me was that all three words began with the prefix "Re." According to the dictionary, "RE" means "'again' or 'again and again' to indicate repetition, or with the meaning 'back' or 'backward' to indicate withdrawal or backward motion."[4]

Again, and again and again! It kept ringing through my ears and I pressed into God for more insight. What exactly does He mean by, "again?" Not once, not twice, but again!

After many days and nights seeking the Lord, He began to reveal to me a picture of health. First, we must *restore* our body, soul, and spirit. To restore means to bring back to its intended design. Many of us have spent years upon years with bad eating habits and a toxic thought life. Some may not even remember a time where they felt whole in body, soul, or spirit. However, I have never met a patient who was too far from the grace of God! Restoration is available to all of us! It will take work, sacrifice, and diligence, but God is always faithful to lead us along the journey and bring us back to His intended design for us.

Restoration is a double-sided tool! Not only does it bring unifying strength to our own life, but it becomes a gift and access point to reveal to others what restoration looks like and to call them in and up towards that place as well! When restoration and joy comes, it spills over to others.

Second is *rebuild.* Picture an old, deserted house that has been abandoned for decades. The house is in shambles, dirt and dust cover the floors and the walls. The concrete has cracks and the frames are unsteady. Remnants of past inhibitors are left behind and it feels

4 http://www.dictionary.com/browse/re-

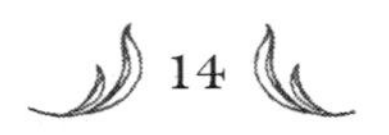

as if it could collapse any second. In order to begin the rebuilding process, the house must be completely torn down in order to rebuild. We now have a completely blank canvas to work with. We must now replace old mindsets and habits with new. Creating a new way of life creates a new foundation for which our destiny can now rest upon. The rebuilding phase is what sets the course for our durability for what is to come.

The third is *refresh.* To refresh means to re-invigorate. Refreshment is what keeps us from burnout. It's important for us to quiet our hearts and reflect on why we are doing what we are doing. Pastor Bill Johnson of Bethel Church is known for his love and appreciation of testimonies of what God has done in people's lives. He believes that a testimony is an invitation for God to do it again. There are some Sundays where he feels lead to spend the entire service sharing testimonies and releasing it over the congregation who need breakthrough in their lives. What he is doing is stirring excitement in the hearts of people by helping build their faith. If God did it once, He will do it again! This is the heart behind the refresh stage; it brings our body, mind, and spirit into alignment with Heaven.

As you go through this book, we are going to go on a journey together through each of the three stages. You will see that each stage will walk you through healing in your body, mind, and spirit.

Before we dig into the book, I want to go over some other key words that I believe will help build you in your pursuit towards wholeness.

Let's start with the word "*Recognition*" or "*Recognize.*" You've heard the old saying. "The first step is admitting that you have a problem." Well, it's true! It is critical that we recognize and identify that we have an issue or that there is a problem before it can be fully addressed. Recognition gives you the opportunity for discernment to be present in your life.

Looking at Isaiah 5:13 we read, "My people have gone into jail because they have no knowledge." The Lord says it clearly that because they don't know Him, His word, or know His voice that they get lead into captivity. The word "knowledge" in the Hebrew means "intimacy, deep, wonderful and great intimacy." There is this discernment that comes in the knowing and in that intimacy we discover new places in ourselves. We discover our needs, strengths, dreams, and so much more. So knowledge comes and it takes the past and it brings it to the present. Knowledge connects and ties our past to our present. And then we take wisdom that comes from the knowledge and we have the ability to take the wisdom that we receive and apply it for the benefit of our future and it changes our circumstances. So recognition is to be able to acknowledge an issue that will lead us to freedom.

"My people are destroyed for lack of knowledge: because thou hast rejected knowledge, I will also reject thee, that thou shalt be no priest to me: seeing thou hast forgotten the law of thy God, I will also forget thy children."
Hosea 4:6

The next word is "*Responsibility.*" After we acknowledge where we are, we have to be willing to take responsibility for it. I want to say that I do recognize that many people go through traumatic and life altering circumstances such as abusive parents, being taken advantage of, and being oppressed. I do not want them to feel as if I am blaming them for their experiences! I believe that the heart of God was not for them to have to endure that, but it is for them to experience healing from it! We can all take responsibility for what we are carrying and be willing to move forward.

In Matthew 11:17, Jesus said, "He who has ears to hear let him hear."[5] In life we hear many different messages from many different sources. First and foremost, we must recognize, hear and follow the Lord's voice. We also hear from others. Whenever we are privileged to hear from the pulpit, you are feeding on knowledge and understanding in a subject. You then become responsible for it and how to integrate it into your life. It can take your past and bring it into your present and propel you into your future for changed realities, which translate into wellness! That is so fabulous!

An example of this with the body aspect is sugar. I learned years and years ago that sugar feeds cancer. So if sugar feeds cancer and I now have knowledge that sugar feeds cancer. It is now my responsibility to use that knowledge to bring healing to my body by limiting my sugar intake.

An example of responsibility in the soul and spirit aspect is anger. I personally grew up very angry, bitter and mad at the world. So the Lord took that passion for being angry and transformed it into a passionate explosion for love in my life. But that anger birthed early in my life within me knows how to trigger a biological cascade that wants to kill me, literally! I have learned that I have a chance daily to partner with it or with love. The word makes it clear that we are to not sin in our anger.[6] I had to recognize that I had an anger problem and take responsibility for it. I had to recognize that at some point, I allowed anger to have control in my life and I had to commit to taking that power back.

This seems to be where most people have the hardest time. In my 20-plus years of practice, I've learned that that not everyone wants to take responsibility. I've heard so many people say, "Well, that is just the way that I am and if God wants to change me, then He will have

---

5 ESV

6 Ephesians 4:26

to do it." This statement couldn't be further from the truth! It is our responsibility! Is it challenging? Yes! However, when we partner with the Holy Spirit, anything is possible! 2 Corinthians 3:18 reads, "But we all, with unveiled faces beholding as in a mirror the glory of the Lord, are transformed into the image from glory to glory, even as from the Lord the Spirit." It is indeed our responsibility to change and to be transformed! We are not created to be static.

I want His infallible truth and His love for me to pierce in the depths of me. My hearts cry is to be just like Jesus. I believe that we should all aim to become more like Jesus everyday and we are to ask God to reveal to us what needs to change in our lives in order to do so.

We know that there is no condemnation, but sometimes we are required to repent for participating in something that you know does not align with God.

That brings me to our next "RE" word. *Repent.* Repent means "to change your mind." Repentance requires action. In Acts 3:19 we read, "Repent, then, and turn to God, so that your sins may be wiped out, those times of refreshing may come from the Lord."

It is said that it is His kindness that leads us into repentance. I have come to love seeking the presence of the Lord because when we find His presence, we find His love and gentleness. When I am in his presence, there is no coercion. His goodness makes me want to step into being fully repentant so that I can change my direction if I am in the wrong. In Nehemiah we read the story of the Israelites. They knew that they needed God to intervene, so they stood in their places and confessed their sins and the sins of their ancestors. Sure enough, freedom came for them. I am just in awe of that. Can you imagine every Christian repenting from his or her sins and experiencing the forgiveness the Lord offers? Like the Israelites, we are to release our past because we recognize that there was something holding us back.

Once released, we can move forward in our freedom and destiny. I don't know about you, but that makes me want to shout a loud "YES" for repentance!

The enemy recognizes the power of repentance and his strategy is to try to place shame and fear in the hearts of people. Shame keeps us from wanting to repent because we fear what others may think of us. I personally battled this and I remember the first time I had to give my testimony to someone. I was so ashamed at some of the roads I took in life. I even felt ashamed about some of the situations that had happened to me that I had no control over! But since I had carried those burdens and secrets since childhood, I allowed shame to weigh me down and keep me silent. So when I finally started to give my testimony and give my heart a voice, I was overcome with freedom! You see, Satan wants to keep us bound by keeping our mouth shut. So, he brings fear, shame, guilt and condemnation, instead of righteousness, joy and peace. I was bound, but I recognized it, took responsibility, repented and stepped forward into freedom! Freedom comes in giving voice to your story.

Now, just because we repent doesn't mean that things we have processed or repented of don't come up again. I have had opportunities to revisit things in my life. This isn't necessarily a bad thing because in doing so, we have the opportunity to receive more breakthrough! Freedom sometimes comes progressively and if we determine we have received all the freedom we could possibly have in an area of our lives, we close ourselves off to the "more" that is always available in God.

Foundationally, it is important to know that from the moment of salvation, Heaven looks at you as if you've never sinned. From that point forward, our job is to be holy and to sanctify ourselves with the Lord.

The next RE word is "*Rejoicing*." I believe that living in a place of praise and gratitude towards God is vital for our health! It is good to give thanks to God because He is worthy of our praise in power and majesty! We see the power of rejoicing in Isaiah 35 that reads:

And a highway will be there;
it will be called the Way of Holiness;
it will be for those who walk on that Way.
The unclean will not journey on it;
wicked fools will not go about on it.
9 No lion will be there,
nor any ravenous beast;
they will not be found there.
But only the redeemed will walk there,
and those the Lord has rescued will return.
They will enter Zion with singing;
everlasting joy will crown their heads.
Gladness and joy will overtake them,
and sorrow and sighing will flee away.

Hallelujah! We have found the highway of holiness that brings streams in the desert! Streams overflowing and it will bring such joy and gladness to your heart. Psalms 22:3 says, "He inhabits the praises of His people." If you want Him near, then praise and rejoice in Him! His presence transcends when you rejoice and praise Him. Rejoice in the Lord always!

As you can see, God has a heart for restoration and bringing us to a place where we can live to our fullest potential. As we take this journey together, I encourage you to allow yourself the grace to explore and discover new and exciting aspects of yourself and the Lord. This journey is just that. A journey. It will take some walking, some exploring, and maybe even some backtracking, but always keep the final destination at the forefront of your heart. You have everything that it takes to succeed, because you have access to the Lord.

Footnotes: "A More Excellent Way" by Henry Wright" Pathways to Wholeness" from Restoration Christian ministries.

	BODY	SOUL	SPIRIT
RESTORE	S.A.D. Lectins/Polyphenols Fiber Water Multi-vitamin/ mineral	Great Commandment Generations Remember who you are God Consciousness The Re's 7 steps to sin The Father's Love	Meditating on the Word Declaration of the Word Praying in the Spirit Church and community
REBUILD	Exercise Enzymes/HCL Pepsin Probiotics Immunity Chiropractic Cleanses	Taking thoughts captive Sin in the flesh I choose to forgive Position/Condition Ever Present Golgotha	Prayer Fasting Spiritual Hunger Journaling Cheer myself up (laughter)
REFRESH	Antioxidants Hormones Rest Sunlight Ionization	Armor Up Unplugging Releasing with oils Self-discipline Identity Pathways to Wholeness Sozo	Thankfulness Praise Worship Creativity Shout to the Lord Communion Where's your towel?

Chapter 2

HOW TO USE THIS BOOK

As I sat down to write this book, I couldn't help but think of all the precious hands that would one day be holding it. Each and every person who reads this will have a different story that comes with different concerns, goals, and outcomes. Therefore, every person's journey through this book is going to be different.

Throughout the course of my career, I have witnessed first hand people finding complete healing and wholeness by practicing what I am about to share with you. It will take work, dedication, and the willingness to change on your part. However, I have also noticed that those who were the most successful were the ones who partnered with the Holy Spirit throughout their journey.

As you saw in the previous chapter, I provided you with a grid that outlines the three *RE* words that we are going to be focusing on. Before we begin, your job is going to be to ask the Holy Spirit which *RE*-word you are to start with. Are you in a season where you need to *restore, rebuild, or refresh?* Depending on what you hear from the Holy Spirit, I encourage you to start with the section you feel He is pulling you towards.

Remember that this is a journey that you are about to take. There isn't going to be anyone timing you and pushing you to go faster than you feel comfortable with. You may find that the Holy Spirit will encourage you to stay focused on one chapter for days, weeks, or even a month. Don't be afraid to go at your own pace as long as you're staying steadfast with the Lord.

Take a moment to get quiet before God and ask Him where you are to begin your journey. When you are ready, let's begin…

Section 1

"I will restore to you the years that the swarming locust has eaten, the hopper, the destroyer, and the cutter, my great army, which I sent among you. "You shall eat in plenty and be satisfied, and praise the name of the LORD your God, who has dealt wondrously with you. And my people shall never again be put to shame."

Joel 2:25-26 ESV

//

Before we can begin to plant new seeds of life within our bodies, we must first restore what has been broken. The Lord's heart is for restoration. We were born into a world filled with sin and disease. Jesus paid the ultimate sacrifice to set us free from the bondage of sin. The price has been paid! It is now our responsibility to receive and steward the restoration that he has provided. Let's explore what it looks like to restore your body, soul, and your spirit.

Chapter 3

RESTORE YOUR BODY

We begin with the body because that is where we live – and practically speaking, where we "feel" and measure our health! Before we begin to discuss how to address wellness in the body, I want to share with you how we assess health. As chiropractors, my husband and I have both treated thousands and thousands of patients and it is clear most people come to the clinic because of the pain that they are experiencing in their body. Pain is a powerful and provoking motivator! When a new patient comes to our clinic, they complete a history that includes the typical physical intake you find in most medical offices, but there is also an extensive history taken concerning an individual's soul and spirit history in regards to their health. This history intake helps us get a snapshot of what's going on inside of you as well as taking a look at your family genetics. The intake delves into spiritual background and practices as well as the history and state of your soul. Collectively, these three inquiries provide a much better reflection of an individual's state of wellness and how they can be better helped than the traditional model.

Physiologically, our bodies are controlled largely by our brain and spinal cord, which make up the central nervous system. The nervous system is the master system that controls all other systems of the body. Under the control of the central nervous system are the:

/ Cardiovascular system
/ Digestive system
/ Hepatic system
/ Renal system
/ Pulmonary system
/ Musculoskeletal system
/ Endocrine system
/ Immune system.

Each of these are all related and interrelated within the body and function collectively to allow our bodies to thrive or fail when one or more systems are in need of help.

Brain Gut Immune Axis

I have found that stress is the biggest robber of health! Stress comes clothed in a variety of costumes and it's important to be able to recognize them. When there is physical stress on the body (whether actual or perceived) it really is a spirit of fear. Thankfully, there are solutions for addressing it in the body, soul, and spirit.

We begin with the Brain Digestive Immune Axis and how that plays into overall health. One of the most health-alternating conditions is stress! When your body is under stress, it cannot function at its fullest capacity! It begins when there is a stressor (perceived or physical) placed on your body. In response, your brain sends signals to your gut and causes almost immediate changes to your gut bacteria population, which strongly influences your immune system. The progression then develops to the emergency stage.

Research done by Hans Selye, a Hungarian endocrinologist, researched stress and determined that there is what we call "General Adaptation Syndrome." This syndrome outlines the cycle of stress and he discovered that it has three stages. He states that "First there is an 'alarm reaction,' in which the body prepares itself for 'fight or flight.' No organism can sustain this condition of excitement, however, and a second stage of adaptation ensues (provided the organism survives the first stage). In the second stage, a resistance to the stress is built. Finally, if the duration of the stress is sufficiently long, the body eventually enters a stage of exhaustion, a sort of aging due to wear and tear."[7]

So for simplicity, take this picture of a heartbeat. A heartbeat resets itself coming back to the baseline, which is the activity of your "fight or flight" mechanism. This "fight or flight" mechanism was designed to reset because we are designed to handle stressors in life. Now, we were not meant to handle extreme stressors day in and day out! This photo represents the resistance stage. In this stage, it doesn't reset like the alarm stage, rather it just goes up and stays up. When your body cannot operate at this stage any longer, you arrive at the exhaustion stage.

The resistance stage produces a series of chemical reactions that communicate to the gut. The gut then communicates to the immune system and inflammatory system. This is when your will notice your body having more aches and pains and your body then reaches the exhaustion stage where sicknesses and disease surface.

---

7 http://brainconnection.brainhq.com/2013/04/05/hans-selye-the-discovery-of-stress/

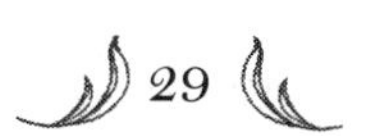

This process can occur at the physical level with physical stressors. However, it can also occur within the soul and spirit level, which will produce physical or perceived stressors all of which require care and correction.

This is why it is important that we look at what enhances the body's wellness as well as what can harm your body so that we can make lifestyle changes that will fully restore wellness. To fully understand what this education process looks like, allow me to introduce you to something called "Neuroplasticity." By definition, it is the brains ability to re-organize itself by forming new neural connections throughout life.[8] This can be used either positively or negatively.

To explain neuroplasticity, I will use the simple example of my personal desire to play piano. I have a great desire to play the piano like George Winston!

I admire him and his work and would give anything to be able to play the piano as he does! I wasn't born with a God-given gift to be able to suddenly play an instrument by just sitting down with it. No, no. If I want to be able to someday play like Mr. Winston, I must have a game plan. Here is my progress in that direction:

Step one: Buy a piano.
Step two: Take lessons.
Step three: Practice, practice, practice!

As I practice, I am creating new neural connections in my brain that place my ability to play in the short term memory part of my brain. As I continue to practice, the neuroplasticity will eventually move out of short-term memory into long-term memory and will then become a permanent part of my biology.

That's just an example of how neuroplasticity works and how it

8 http://www.medicinenet.com/script/main/art.asp?articlekey=40362

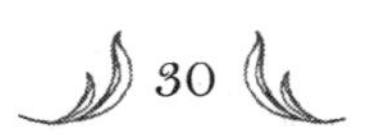

becomes a permanent part of your brain. Now, allow me to show you how neuroplasticity works when engaged with the body, soul, and spirit.

An example is how your brain processed emotions. In the early stages of your life, your brain processes your life experiences. In those first five years, there's so much information going in and out of your brain and this is when you learn how to process emotions like love and hate. It all comes down to the circumstances you grew up in. The neuroplasticity of those emotions and experiences you encountered began to form and became a permanent part of your biology. It's not because you wanted them to be but because that's what you were taught. When you have an emotional implantation at that level, many times you don't even realize how to move past it and create new pathways. The good news is, you can!

Neuroplasticity, on a spiritual level, gives you new brain connections and shuts down old pathways of thinking. It makes your spirit-man come alive and gives you strategy to overcome obstacles. Because of this, we can actually restore our brain patterns to become aligned with Heaven!

The American Diet

It is impossible to restore the body without addressing our diet. As a culture, we have become completely oblivious and frankly, irresponsible when it comes to what we put inside our bodies. Did you know that the acronym for the Standard American Diet is curiously reflective of itself: SAD! I couldn't agree more!

The American diet is very sad from a health perspective! Our grocery stores are loaded with "foods" that are filled with additives and preservatives, which contribute to disease and illness. I always advise my patients to shop the perimeter of the grocery store where we can find foods that we were designed to eat and thrive on. Foods that are alive and filled with nutrients and fiber that best support our bodies.

Calorie Breakdown Madness

According to the USDA, nearly 1,000 calories a day (out of a 2775 daily calorie diet) is attributed to added fats and sweeteners! In comparison, dairy, fruits and vegetables only contribute 424 calories. Our priorities for food are simply out of balance.

Daily calories per capita by food group, 2010

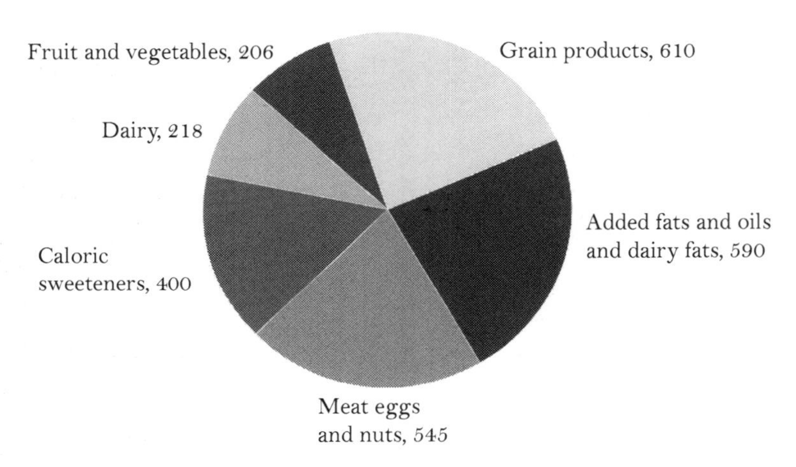

Added fats and oils and caloric sweeteners are added to food during processing or preparation. They do not include naturally occurring fats and sugars in food (e.g., fats in meat or sugars in fruits).
Source: USDA, Economic Research Service, Loss-Adjusted Food Availability Data.
[Original Chart: http://www.ers.usda.gov/media/1188540/food-availability_fig04.png]

In fact, 38% of adults in the U.S. report consuming fruits less than one time daily, and less than 22% report eating vegetables daily.

While adolescents do fare better in the vegetable category, this may be attributable to unhealthy fried vegetables (i.e. French fries) and other processed vegetables available at school.

Oregon and California stand ahead of the rest of the country. Adults in these states eat vegetables 1.8 or more times per day. Meanwhile, adults in five states report eating vegetables less than 1.5 times per day.[9]

As of 2000, Americans were consuming nearly 200 pounds of grain per year, the vast majority from wheat flour. It's important to note that while we are consuming considerably more wheat, we must take into account that it isn't the same wheat we once ate. Today, according to the Journal of Trace Elements in Medicine and Biology, the mineral density of wheat has dramatically declined in the last 20 years.

World Grain Production, Consumption and Stocks

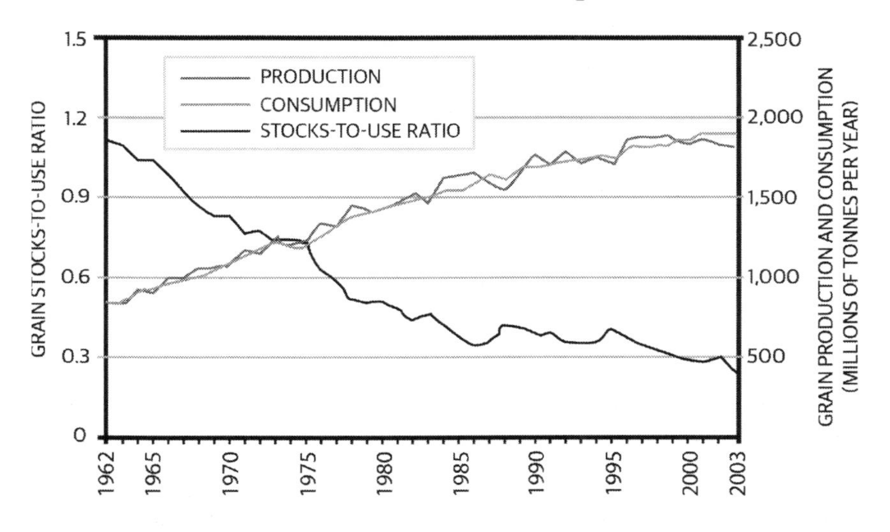

Source: UN FAO Food Outlook Dec. 2003

9 https://www.cdc.gov/nutrition/downloads/state-indicator-report-fruits-vegetables-2013.pdf

The wheat of today has nearly 30% less minerals! Why is the wheat we eat today less nutritious than before? The answer: GMOs. Researchers believe that the significant increase in the number of individuals with celiac disease and gluten intolerance is a result of nutritionally bankrupt wheat, as well as the dramatic increase in its consumption.

Today, nearly 80% of Americans are magnesium deficient, leading to leg cramps, insomnia, fibromyalgia, high blood pressure and osteoporosis. An additional study found that phytic acid also inhibits the absorption of zinc and calcium resulting in loss of bone density, loose teeth and tooth decay.

Decreases in Fruit and Vegetable Intake

Leafy green vegetables, squash, root vegetables, asparagus, artichokes, and others provide essential nutrients for our bodies. I strongly support juicing vegetables to boost health. Juicing fruits and vegetables helps to make them easier to digest and absorb into your system. Vitamin C, E, essential B vitamins and a whole host of minerals are crucial to good health and are easily incorporated into your diet.

Median Daily Vegetable Intake Among Adults in the United States

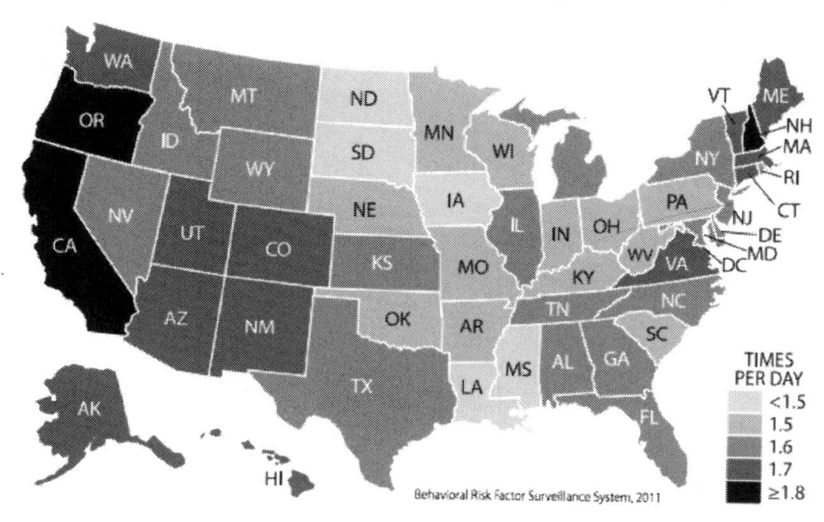

Source: http://www.cdc.gov/nutrition/downloads/State-Indicator-Report-Fruits-Vegetables-2013.pdf

Combining vegetables allows you to increase the intake of essential nutrients, helping to aid in digestion, improve energy, lose stubborn weight, strengthen your immune system, and lessen your risks for developing chronic diseases like cancer, heart disease and Type 2 diabetes.

Consumption of Sugar Has Skyrocketed

In the last 65 years, not only has the amount of sugar we eat dramatically increased, the source of the sugar has radically changed! In the 1950s, the majority of the sugar consumed by Americans was from cane and beet sugar.

US Sugar Consumption, 1822-2005

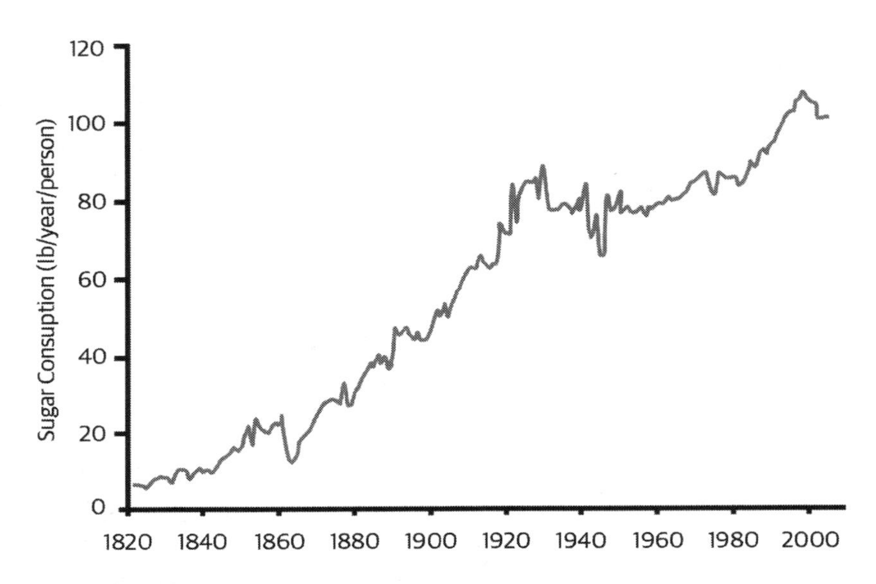

Source: Stephan Guyenet and Jeremy Landen, http://wholehealthsource.blogspot.com

In 2000, according to the USDA, each individual in the U.S. consumed over 150 pounds of sugar. Over half of that came from corn! Just because high-fructose sugar is made from corn doesn't mean that it is a healthy sweetener.

Over the last hundred years, our taste buds have changed. Today everything needs to be super-sweet, even foods we don't tend to think as sweet. Traditional wheat-based breads, for example, contain sugar. While sugar is important for fermentation and getting yeast to activate, the next time you reach for a loaf of "honey whole wheat," check the label. It may surprise you! Each slice has three grams of sugar, sourced from both honey and refined sugar.

Processed Foods Make Up 63 Percent of Calories

This chart shows that 63% of calories Americans are consuming today are coming from processed foods. Convenience foods are packed with preservatives, added oils, sugars and refined grains — none of which is healthy for the body, as these foods definitely do more harm than good.

U.S Food Consumption As A% of Calories

Plant Food:
Vegetables, Fruits, Legumes, Nuts & Seeds, Whole Grains
Fiber is only found in plant foods

Note: Up to half of this category may be processed, for example almonds in candy bars, apples in apple pies or spinach in frozen spinach soufflé, and of course these would not be healthy choices. The focus should be on whole unprocessed vegetables, fruits, legumes, nuts and seeds and whole grains.

Processed Food:
Added Fats & Oils, Sugars, Refined Grains

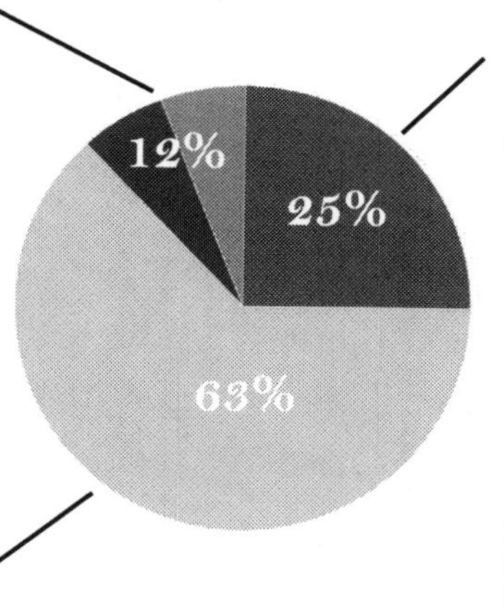

Animal Food:
Meat, Dairy, Eggs, Fish, Seafood. *Cholesterol is only found in animal foods. Animal foods are the PRIMARY source of saturated fat.*

Guide to Healthy Eating:
Much easier to understand the USDA food Pyramid, with no food industry influence.

Eat **LESS** from the animal and processed groups and **MORE** whole foods from the plant food group.

In general, food from the animal and processed food group contribute to disease, while **WHOLE** foods from plant group contribute to good health.

Source: USDA, Economic Research Service, 2009
http://www.nyu.edu/sustainability/pdf/NYCHSF_FoodGraph2.pdf

Sadly, plant-based foods are only making up 12 percent of calories consumed in the U.S. today. The statement at the top right of this graph is misleading, but nonetheless shows that even organizations that are trying to get us to eat healthier often miss the overall picture.

So, in order to understand why foods can be harming us it is important to look at the trends. It is shocking to observe the empty calories and "dead" food trend that we have adopted as the focal point of our nutritional intake. With this knowledge as the backdrop, I will provide for you insight as to the consequence and impact of these food choices have over time on our bodies. https://draxe.com/charts-american-diet/

Foods to Avoid and Foods to Enjoy!

LECTINS (Avoid)

What's a lectin? I personally believe that lectins are one of the single worst things that we can put into our bodies. They are powerful toxic allergens and found in many of the foods that you eat every day. So much press has been given to gluten allergies to the point where an entire industry has evolved to meet the need of those with gluten allergies. However, lectins can create a far more dangerous allergic reaction than gluten does.

The Lectin Report:

Lectins were first described in 1888 by Stillmark working with castor bean extracts. Many members of the lectinic protein family agglutinate (clump together) red blood cells. Research done by Ehrlich, considered to be the father of immunology, has shown that feeding small amounts of lectin containing seeds to rabbits caused partial immunity to the toxicity demonstrating lectins are also antigenic (able to induce antigen antibody reactions).[10]

One of the dangers that lectins present are a disruption to your immune system and they prevent your body from healing itself. But even more significantly, they have the capacity to breakthrough and pierce the intestinal barrier and cause leaky gut syndrome. When your intestinal barrier is pierced, small particles of toxic bacteria get through which then causes massive inflammation to most every part of your body. With inflammation comes muscle and joint pain, obesity, arthritis, kidney failure, skin disorders, eczema, psoriasis, and painful digestive disorders. When your body is inflamed it has to work "overtime," thus draining your body of the energy it needs to sustain health and vibrancy. They actually weaken your blood vessels which is a condition called endothelial dysfunction. This is a serious condition linked not only to hypertension and heart disease, but diabetes, obesity and septic shock as well. People eating a diet high in lectin can also experience all kinds of cardiovascular disease and endothelial dysfunction.

So, what foods actually contain lectin?

/ All grains.
/ Nightshades including tomato, peppers, potato and eggplant.
/ Gluten found in wheat, rye, barley, malt, and maybe oats.
/ Legumes- all beans including soy and peanut.
/ Dairy including all milk products, milk, cheese, cottage cheese, yogurt, kefir.
/ Yeast (except brewer's and nutritional).

10 http://www.krispin.com/lectin.html

I encourage you that when you look at a healthy diet, it is vital to minimize lectin in order to improve your body's ability to be well.

Polyphenols (Enjoy)

A big word with a powerful punch! Polyphenols are phytochemicals, meaning compounds found abundantly in natural plant food sources that have antioxidant properties. There are over 8,000 identified polyphenols found in foods such as tea, wine, chocolates, fruits, vegetables, and extra virgin olive oil, just to name a few! The strongest sources of polyphenols include:

/ Mulberries
/ Antonia cherries
/ Bilberries
/ Acai berries
/ Berberine extract
/ Blue berries
/ Cranberries
/ Pomegranate
/ Blackberries
/ Fruits and vegetables

These play an important role in maintaining your health and wellness. Antioxidants help protect the cells in your body from free-radical damage, thereby controlling the rate at which you age! It's nature's fountain of youth! They are the most important ingredient that you're most likely not getting in your diet in large quantities. I encourage you to include polyphenols in your diet as much as possible! Polyphenols are incredibly potent so when these micronutrients are ingested into the human body they become huge energy boosters! This is especially important because most people are suffering from dangerously low energy (hence why it seems most everyone has a caffeine addiction). In fact, their impact is much broader than just energy including:

/ Boosts metabolic function
/ Fights inflammation in almost every part of your body.
/ Reduces the signs of aging
/ Lowers cholesterol
/ Regulates blood sugar levels
/ Boosts the immune system
/ Reduces joint pain
/ Reduces digestive discomfort
/ Keeps your skin healthy and firm
/ Boosts your metabolism

It's important to note that back in the day people had more energy. This is because people only ate what they hunted and gathered and meat was only 10% of their diet! They thrived off leafy greens and roots that grew in the ground, fruits and nuts that grew in trees and a large percentage of their diet came from berries of all sorts which are packed full of polyphenols! Lots and lots of berries! Then, we invented agriculture, which included barley and wheat.

With that said, before agriculture the plant polyphenols were converted into energy for the body. After the agriculture movement, grains were harvested which are considered empty carbs because once ingested, they are then converted into fat. As a result, many of us are now struggling with low energy, a slow metabolism, and weight gain. Polyphenols are little miracle organisms because they not only make you feel better; they also help you live longer!

Consider polyphenols as fuel for your body. More specifically, they are fuel for the microorganisms in your digestive system known as probiotics. Your intestines have huge colonies of probiotics that help you digest your favorite foods without gas, bloating, abdominal discomfort, constipation, or diarrhea. Probiotics are a Godsend but they need a constant supply of fuel to be able to do their work and polyphenols are what they eat.

The polyphenols found in fruits and vegetables are broken down by bacteria in the colon. Studies have shown that they influence the microorganisms for use as ingredients in functional foods that promote good health. These bacterias are not only essential to good digestion, but to your immune system as well. 70% of your immune system lives in your digestive tract! It is important for cellular energy and well worth taking care of!

However, the standard American diet is extremely low in plant polyphenols! Because of this, we are experiencing an epidemic of polyphenol deficiency that contributes to many of the modern health problems that plaque America. We need to begin to make an effort to include high polyphenol foods in our diet.

FIBER (Enjoy)

We've all heard that fiber is an essential part of a healthy diet. But what exactly is fiber? Fiber is a part of the structure of plants that helps build plant molecules, including cellulose, lignin and pectin. Fiber actually contains zero calories since humans essentially can't digest it. Although it's found in carbohydrate-rich foods such as vegetables, fruits, nuts and whole grains, it doesn't contribute any carbs to our diets.

Fiber is packed full with health benefits for our bodies and is most essential for our gut health. Dietary fiber promotes health by fueling beneficial bacteria to produce compounds that help regulate your immune function and push toxins out of our bodies.

The FDA recommends 30 to 32 grams of fiber per day, but very few people in our country are taking that in! Unfortunately, when our fiber intake is lacking, it then starves the good bacteria in our system, which thereby sends your health into a downward spiral. Not only does this affect the immune system and promotes autoimmune diseases, but it also results in the breakdown of your gut barrier which then leads to inflammation with an increased risk of inflammatory diseases.

There are so many benefits to having a diet high in fiber, which may include:

/ Balanced blood sugar levels
/ Improved Heart health
/ Decreased risk of stroke
/ Weight loss
/ Improved skin health
/ Decreased risk of Diverticulitis
/ Decreased risk of Hemorrhoids
/ Relieves IBS (Irritable Bowel Syndrome)
/ Reduced risk of gallstones and kidney stones

As you can see, many health benefits are associated with fiber with its impact specifically on the microbes in your gut. Not only does soluble fiber serve as a prebiotic, but it also converts short chain fatty acids that are then converted to healthy ketones that feed your tissues. In essence we have strayed too far from our natural diet, which promotes healthy gut flora.

Foods high in fiber:

/ Artichokes
Fiber: 10.3 grams per medium vegetable, cooked.

/ Peas
Fiber: 8.8 grams per cup, cooked.

/ Broccoli
Fiber: 5.1 grams per cup, boiled.

/ Brussels Sprouts
Fiber: 4.1 grams per cup, boiled

/ Avocados
Fiber: 6.7 grams per half, raw.

/ Turnips
Fiber: 4.8 grams of fiber per ½ cup

/ Okra
Fiber: 8.2 grams per cup

/ Raspberries
Fiber: 8 grams per cup, raw.

/ Blackberries
Fiber: 7.6 grams per cup, raw.

/ Pears
Fiber: 5.5 grams per medium fruit, raw.

/ Figs
Fiber: 14.6 grams of fiber in 1 cup dried figs

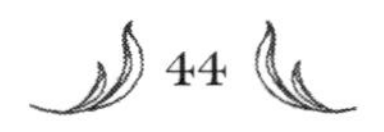

/ Nuts
Fiber: 0.6 grams of fiber per 6 almonds

/ Walnut
Fiber: 1.9 grams of fiber per 1 ounce by weight

Water (Enjoy! A LOT)

It goes without saying that drinking water is essential for our health! Why is drinking water so important? For a start, 60% of your body is made up of water, so it's essential to keep the body working properly.[11] When the body's water requirement is not met, it has a variety of negative short-term and long-term health consequences.

Long-term dehydration can lead to rheumatoid arthritis, migraines, angina, colitis, dyspepsia, hypertension, obesity, hemorrhoids, breast cancer, pulmonary tuberculosis, kidney stones, sinusitis, and uterine cancers!

Water is your ally when it comes to helping fight off disease and inflammation! It's up to us to make sure we are keeping our bodies well hydrated so it can function at it's fullest.

When I meet with patients that have struggle with health conditions, I like to recommend that they become intentional about their water intake and even do what I call a water treatment. A water treatment is a proven method for treating body disorders, menstrual disorders, and eye-related ailments. Many patients have reported feeling invigorated within 24 hours after following this water treatment.

To perform this water treatment, begin by drinking approximately 160 ml of water four times immediately after waking up, before brushing your teeth and on an empty stomach. If you

11 https://water.usgs.gov/edu/propertyyou.html

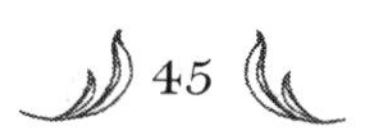

cannot drink four glasses of water on an empty stomach, then you can begin with one glass and work your way up. Allow your body to restore and re-hydrate properly by not eating anything for the next 45 minutes. Before eating, have another glass of water. Continue to drink water at least 30 minutes before every meal, but not during the following two hours after breakfast, lunch, and dinner. This is important because drinking too much water after eating will disrupt your digestive cycle and dilute your body's natural digestive acids and enzymes. You can gradually increase the intake of water until you reach the desired level of 640 ml.

If you're not used to drinking water, you're probably wondering how on earth you could ever take in that many fluids! I encourage you to just do the best you can and allow your body to adjust on it's own.

Depending on your health conditions and goals, you can expect to see results in as little as 10-30days. Diabetes or high blood pressure patients, allow 30 days. If you suffer from constipation and gastritis, allow 10 days. If you are struggling with TB, allow 90 days.

Whether you decide to do the water treatment or not, I still strongly encourage you to begin increasing your water intake! I recommend to everyone that they start their day with a large glass of water! Drinking water on an empty stomach is key because it allows the body to flush out toxins at a more rapid pace. It also naturally stimulates movement in your bowels. At night, your body repairs itself and casts out all the toxins in your body, so when you drink water on an empty stomach in the morning, you will flush out these harmful toxins, leaving your body fresh and healthy. Drinking plenty of water can also help in increasing the production of muscle cells as well as new blood cells.

www.quantumbalancing.com/japanwatercure.htm

1. Reinforces Healthy Weight Loss

Drinking water on an empty stomach can also help increase your metabolic rate by at least 24%![12] An increased metabolic rate means an improved digestive system. It is very important for those people who are on a strict diet to make sure they are keeping hydrated to help your body in burning fat. Drinking water immediately after waking up also helps purify the colon, making it easier to absorb nutrients. You'll notice that you will also feel less hungry and your cravings will be reduced. This alone helps prevent weight gain caused by overeating.

2. Alleviates Heartburn and Indigestion

Indigestion is caused by increased acidity in the stomach. You'll notice that you suffer from heartburn when the acid refluxes into your esophagus. When you drink water on an empty stomach, these acids are pushed down and gets diluted which solves the problem!

3. Improves Complexion and Skin Radiance

Water is the best-kept secret for youthful, healthy skin! Dehydration causes premature wrinkles and deep pores in the skin. It was found in a study that drinking 500 ml of water on an empty stomach increases blood flow in the skin and makes skin glow![13] Also, drinking more water throughout the day means that your body is releasing toxins, which will make your skin more radiant.

12 https://www.curejoy.com/content/benefits-drinking-water-empty-stomach/
13 http://justhealthlifestyle.com/health-benefits-of-drinking-water-on-an-empty-stomach/

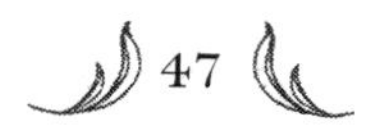

4. Promotes Shiny, Smooth, and Healthy Hair

Dehydration can have a serious impact on your hair growth. Drinking plenty of water nourishes your hair from the inside out. Water makes up almost ¼ of the weight of a hair strand. An insufficient intake of water can cause brittle hair and thin hair strands.

5. Prevents Kidney Stones and Bladder Infections

Drinking water immediately after waking up is important for preventing kidney stones and bladder infections. It is a fact that drinking water on an empty stomach dilutes the acids, which lead to stones in the kidney. The more water you drink (to a healthy limit), the more you will be protected from various kinds of bladder infections caused by toxins.

6. Strengthens Immune System

Drinking water on an empty stomach helps in flushing and balancing the lymphatic system, which leads to increased levels of immunity. A strong immune system will keep you safe from various diseases and prevent you from falling sick as often.

As you can see, there are a whole host of benefits of drinking water immediately after waking up! It's without a doubt the easiest way to make a positive change to your lifestyle without spending any money. Water is the solvent in our bodies, and as such, it regulates all the functions of our bodies. In fact, every function of the body is monitored and pegged to the efficient flow of water – throughout the body and in and out of every cell. Think for a moment of just a few of the functions that water regulates:

/ The movement of blood
/ The transport of nutrients into our cells
/ The movement of waste out of our cells
/ The flow of lymph fluid
/ The movement of nerve impulses through our nerves
/ The movement of hormones throughout our bodies
/ The functioning of our brain

It's important to note that our bodies are designed to help keep us alive, which means it can function on very little water for an amount of time. The body quickly adapts and starts extracting more water from your stools, for example. The kidneys flush less water to retain the limited supply you have. In fact, there are some health experts who claim that your body does quite well on 2 glasses of any kind of fluid a day -- plus the water found in the food you eat. But these experts confuse adaptation with health. Adaptation eventually leads to compromise, which leads to diminished health over time.

Look, ultimately it may be proven that drinking more than 2 glasses of water a day has no health benefits, but that day has not arrived yet -- and the Negoianu, Goldfarb review, which claims to have proven that we don't need to drink eight glasses of water a day, does not bring it any closer. It's bad science, bad reporting by the press, and shoddy peer review by the *Journal of the American Society of Nephrology.*

Supplements

There was a time when it took a lot of arguing to convince people to add supplements to their diets. Although people may not know the exact numbers, they are aware that the food that is sold in markets today is less nutritious than it was 50 years ago. For example:

/ It takes 80 cups of today's supermarket spinach to give you the same iron you'd get from just one cup of spinach grown 50 years ago.

/ According to a Rutgers University study, it now takes 19 ears of corn to equal the nutritional value of just one ear of corn grown in 1940.

/ There is less than half the protein in today's wheat as in the wheat our grandparents ate.

/ Much of our soil is so depleted that our farm crops depend ENTIRELY on the chemical fertilizers they are fed to grow. That means that most of the food we eat is devoid of virtually all the trace minerals we need for survival.

When you look at the statistics, it doesn't take a rocket scientist to figure out what's happened. We've exchanged quality for quantity and we are now paying the price. You can't increase your yield per acre while at the same time steadily depleting your soil year after year and not expect to lose something in the process. And what's been lost is the quality of our food.

The bottom line is that if you live in any industrialized country in the world today, you must add supplements to maintain your health. With the right supplements, you can help to reduce the risk of cancer, heart disease, various degenerative diseases, while slowing down the aging process, and protect yourself against toxic injury!

jonbarron.org/dietary-supplements/what-supplements-to-buy-and-trust

At this point in time, the best supplements are actually "grown" using a live, biodynamic growing process that results in organic food matrix supplements. Instead of being chemically manufactured, this type of supplement is literally created by growing nutritional yeast (or in some cases, probiotics) in a "super-dense nutrient-broth." What you end up with is a "living" vitamin/mineral complex that is comprised of a highly complex interlocking system of vitamins, enzymes, minerals, active bioflavonoid groups, micro proteins, complex carbohydrates, and countless other naturally occurring food constituents. More specifically, the resulting supplement is an organic food matrix consisting of non-denatured, water-soluble nutrients and micro-nutrients molecularly bound into a highly complex interlocking systems of lipoproteins, glycoproteins, phosphoproteins, phospholipids, nucleoproteins, essential fatty acids, complex carbohydrates, numerous enzymes and coenzyme groups, biologically-active bioflavonoid groups, water molecules, and countless other naturally occurring food constituents in an authentic food complex.

Make no mistake, this type of multivitamin/mineral formula is unlike most other supplements you have ever used. Supplements made this way are easily the most body-friendly vitamin/mineral supplement you can find and provides optimum levels of nutrition while avoiding the problems associated with the mega-dosing of synthetic and co-natural vitamins.

I always encourage my patients to look for supplements from the raw, whole food matrix. You don't necessarily have to supplement with a pill. My daily supplement routine is making a super-green shake everyday with added plant proteins as well as extra spinach or kale and polyphenols (berries). This way, I have eliminated my need to take added pills while also increasing my fiber intake!

Enzymes

I cannot stress the importance of enzymes! Many people do not even know what enzymes are, let alone what they do. To put it simply, they are proteins that accelerate biochemical reactions within the body. Enzymes grab onto food or debris causing the reaction digesting the food. Digestive enzymes are utilized to breakdown food in the body and then use it as fuel.

I always say that healthy digestion begins in the mouth! When we chew our food, enzymes are released through our saliva, which begins the pre-digestion phase. This aids in the breakdown of food in the stomach for 45 minutes and can breakdown approximately 75% of food! From there, stomach acid (HCL and pepsin) is released which is when the enzymes stopped being produced. The stomach then breaks down what is left of the food into a healthy food concentrate. From there, the stomach opens into the small intestine and releases the food concentrate. The pancreas then releases bicarbonate and more enzymes to finish further digestion through the intestines. As digestion is finishing, the nutrients are absorbed through the intestinal wall into the blood stream to fuel and nourish the body.

jonbarron.org/digestive-health/digestive-enzymes-healthy-diet

All of that to say that before any food you eat reaches the bodies cells, they need to be broken down. Proteins are turned into amino acids, fats into fatty acids, and carbohydrates into glucose. This natural process is what helps deliver nutrients to our bodies. However, in our culture, many of us don't eat for nourishment but rather for enjoyment.

Herein lies the problem, we were designed to eat to stay alive and not for comfort. Comfort foods generally do not provide adequate nutrition and nourishment that we need to be healthy. They are generally cooked and processed foods. Many people don't realize that cooking food at temperatures over 116-127 degrees Fahrenheit ends up killing the enzymes that occur naturally. Also processed foods (chemically laden to give that fabulous shelf life) have also muddied up the live enzymes needed for digestion as well. Many people eat foods that are seriously devoid of life! When we eat dead food that is lacking in enzymes as well as not supplementing with enzymes, it results in poor digestion. I should also note that it is vitally important that we thoroughly chew our food! This allows the enzymes from our digestion to begin breaking down our food. Food that is not digested creates a hatchery for parasites and microbes to begin infesting the body.

We've covered only a few benefits to taking enzymes. More benefits include:

/ Aiding in digestion and removes burden on the pancreas
/ Reduces indigestion and heartburn
/ Improved digestion of dairy
/ Diminished allergies

/ Decrease in gas and bloating
/ Increase in energy

Dr. Howell once said, "A person's life span is directly related to the exhaustion of their enzyme potential. And the use of food enzymes decreases that rate of exhaustion, and thus, results in a longer, healthier, and more vital life."[14] I couldn't agree more.

HCL with pepsin

I have had patients come to me who have low stomach acid. Many people associate stomach acid with things like heartburn and gas, however having low stomach acid can cause their own set of problems as well! It's important that we have a balanced amount of stomach acid because stomach acid helps break down food. For those who have low stomach acid, I always recommend adding HCL with pepsin (hydrochloric acid with pepsin). Now, hydrochloric acid is naturally created in your stomach. If you're deficient in hydrochloric acid and stomach acid itself, you won't be able to fully digest and break down things like protein, which, over time, can also cause a condition called leaky gut.

Now, the trick with HCL is that you typically want to take it while you're under the care of a physician. I always have my patients start off with one capsule. I should also note that you only take HCL with pepsin if you're having protein during a meal. If you're not having protein in a meal, you don't want to use it. When you feel a warm sensation in your stomach that means you're taking enough. Some people need one capsule; other people may need to take up to

---

14 Dr. Howell's book, Enzyme Nutrition…

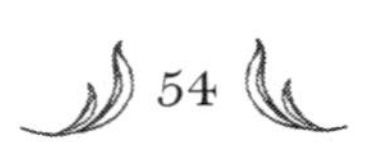

nine capsules of HCL with pepsin. Again, always consult with your doctor before including any supplements into your diet.

Probiotics

It's been said that life and death begins in the colon and I have found that statement to be very true! Some centers, such as Massachusetts Institute of Technology, are now using stool samples as its first line of investigation instead of blood tests in medical cases. This helps them discover the root disease because the gut is our first line of immunity and defense.

Looking at the gut, we find that a properly functioning intestinal tract is one of your body's first lines of defense against invaders and helps create a healthy immune system. In a healthy colon there are anywhere from 100 billion to 1,000 billion beneficial bacteria per milliliter (about 1/5 of a teaspoon) that literally consume harmful bacteria and other invaders. In the typical American citizen, because of poor diet and neglect of the colon, the beneficial bacteria count may be as low as 4 or 5 per milliliter. Just compare 1,000 billion to 4, and you'll have an understanding of the scope and gravity of the problem. Many researchers now believe that declining levels of friendly bacteria in the intestinal tract may actually mark the onset of chronic degenerative disease and a suppressed immune system. Our goal is always to strengthen the immune system.

The benefits of a probiotically optimized intestinal tract include:

- Lowered cholesterol
- Inhibition of cancer
- Protection against food poisoning

/ Protection against stomach ulcers
/ Protection against lactose intolerance and casein intolerance
/ Enhanced immunity
/ Protection against many harmful bacteria, viruses, and fungi
/ Protection against candida overgrowth and vaginal yeast infections
/ Prevention and correction of constipation and diarrhea, ileitis and colitis, irritable bowel syndrome, and a whole range of other digestive tract dysfunctions
/ Improvement in the health and appearance of the skin
/ Better nutrition from improved absorption and the internal generation of B vitamins.
/ Protection against vaginosis and yeast infections

There can be no true health or recovery from disease unless you have colonies of over 100 trillion beneficial microorganisms flourishing in your intestinal tract, from your mouth to your anus, aiding in digestion, absorption, the production of significant amounts of vitamins and enzymes working to crowd out all harmful bacteria -- allowing them no place to gain a foothold.

Please, please do yourself favor and take probiotics everyday

jonbarron.org/detoxing-full-body-detox/probiotics-revisited-part-1

Immunity

To be immune means to be protected. So it makes sense that the body system that helps fight off sickness is called the immune system. The immune system is made up of a network of cells, tissues, and organs that work together to protect the body.

When you get sick, your entire body becomes jeopardized and at an increase risk of further health problems. Some reasons why some people get sick include:

/ Brain imbalance (stress)
/ Toxicities
/ Deficiencies (vitamins and minerals)
/ Lack of Exercise

I am going to camp on the brain imbalance (STRESS) because it is the silent assassin of health! When we are under stress, it begins to fire the sympathetic nervous system. This releases neurotransmitters, epinephrine and norepinephrine. This has a greater effect on the right cortex, which is the emotional/worrisome side of the brain. This only leads to more stress and anxiety, thus beginning the cycle.

The dangerous part about this cycle is that it fires off the adrenal cortex for the release of cortisol. Cortisol is known as the "stress hormone" and is a natural hormone, but can cause problems when over-produced. Cortisol, in turn also drives the right cortex creating more emotion, more worry and more anxiety, which we know is fear based and the opposite of power, love, and a sound mind.

Cortisol will also effect the thyroid stimulating hormone receptors on the thyroid that will slow down the thyroid and lead to thyroid problems. The sluggish thyroid will then have a greater effect on the left cortex causing feelings of sadness, lack of motivation, and a decreased immune response.

The sympathetic nervous system will then shunt blood from the large abdominal veins and arteries that supply the visceral organs, to the arteries and veins of the arms and legs in a fight or flight response. This will cause the digestive system to malfunction if the stress is prolonged (parasympathetic nervous system) and will then get shutdown. The epinephrine and norepinephrine of the sympathetic nervous system will breakdown the glycogen into glucose and cortisol will start gluconeogenesis, meaning sugar is flooding the system. Both cause our blood sugar to elevate and cause depletion in B vitamins, as well as co-factor minerals. This leads to the overall malfunction of all the metabolic systems in the body. All neurons need two things: activation provided by sensory stimuli and fuel provided by glucose. In order to process the glucose properly, you need B vitamins and minerals.

When the depletion is consistent over time, the kreb cycle (life cycle) within the body cannot transfer electrons because vital nutrients are missing in action and no energy is produced. So the sympathetic function continues to fire and no help is available. Excess firing over long periods of time leads to the following:

/ Chronic Fatigue
/ Fibromyalgia
/ Depression
/ Insomnia
/ Obesity
/ GERD
/ Ulcers
/ Irritable Bowel Syndrome

All of this to say, approximately 90% of sickness and disease is said to be a stress related disorder![15] Just type that into web browser and you will be amazed at what you find. In the meantime, here are a few things we can do to help boost our immune system.

Vitamin C

Vitamin C is known for it's immune boosting properties and many people associate it with citrus fruits such as oranges. But did you know that you can also get it from leafy green vegetables such as spinach and kale, bell peppers, brussel sprouts, strawberries and papaya? In fact, vitamin C is in so many foods that most people may not need to take supplements unless a doctor advises it.[16]

Vitamin E

Like vitamin C, vitamin E can be a powerful antioxidant that helps your body fight off infection. Almonds, peanuts, hazelnuts and sunflower seeds are all high in vitamin E. So are spinach and broccoli if you prefer to increase your intake through meals rather than snacks.

Vitamin B6

This important vitamin is part of nearly 200 biochemical reactions in your body and is critical in how your immune system functions. Foods high in vitamin B6 include bananas, lean chicken breast, cold-water fish such as tuna, baked potatoes and chickpeas. Bring on the hummus!

---

15 https://www.ncbi.nlm.nih.gov/pmc/articles/PMC3341916/

16 most people may not need to take supplements

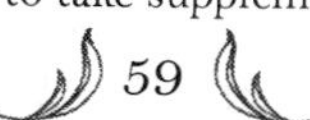

Vitamin A

For vitamin A, go colorful. Foods that are high in colorful compounds called carotenoids (carrots, sweet potatoes, pumpkin, cantaloupe and squash) are all great options. The body turns these carotenoids into vitamin A and they have an antioxidant effect to help strengthen the immune system against infection.

Vitamin D

As mentioned above, it's best to get most of your vitamins from food, but vitamin D may be the exception to that rule. You can increase your intake through foods such as fatty fish (salmon, mackerel, tuna and sardines) and fortified foods such as milk, orange juice and cereals. Many people have a hard time absorbing vitamin D from food; so if you have a vitamin D deficiency, talk to your doctor about supplements.

Folate/folic acid

Folate is the natural form, and folic acid is the synthetic form, often added to foods because of its health benefits. To get more folate, add more beans and peas to your plate on a regular basis, as well as leafy green vegetables. You can also get folic acid in fortified foods (check the label) such as enriched breads, pastas, rice and other 100 percent whole-grain products.

Iron

Iron, which helps your body carry oxygen to cells, comes in different forms. Your body can more easily absorb "heme iron," which is abundant in lean poultry such as chicken and turkey, plus seafood. But never fear, vegetarians: You can get other forms of iron in beans, broccoli and kale.

Selenium

Selenium seems to have a powerful effect on the immune system, including the potential to slow the body's over-active responses to certain aggressive forms of cancer. You can find it in garlic, broccoli, sardines, tuna, brazil nuts and barley, among other foods.

Zinc

You can find zinc in oysters, crab, lean meats and poultry, baked beans (skip the kind with added sugar), yogurt and chickpeas. Zinc appears to help slow down the immune response and control inflammation in your body.[17]

Our goal is to always enhance our immune function by not only adding nutrient-rich foods, but also avoiding nutrient-dead foods. In addition, here are few easy steps:

Avoid Sugar

Sugar decreases the function of your immune system almost immediately!

Get Enough Rest

Just like it becomes harder for you to get your daily tasks done if you're tired, if your body is overly fatigued it will be harder for it to fight off disease. Regular rest will keep you strong and ensure that your body has the strength to fight off any potential invaders.

17 health.clevelandclinic.org/2015/01/eat-these-foods-to-boost-your-immune-system

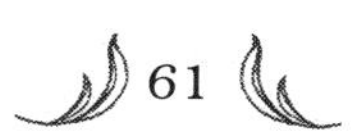

Eat Garlic

Garlic is a triple-whammy: it's antibacterial, antiviral and anti-fungal. Garlic is one food that you should be eating every day. It is important to note that the garlic must be fresh to give you optimal health benefits. The active ingredient is destroyed within one hour of smashing the garlic. Allicin is the active ingredient that is activated with the smashing...so don't eat the clove whole.

Don't Stress

We all face some stress everyday, but if stress becomes overwhelming then your body will be less able to fight off illnesses. It has been estimated that up to 90 percent of illness and disease is stress-related.

Wash Your Hands

Washing your hands will decrease your likelihood of spreading a virus to your nose and mouth. If your immune system is strong, it should be able to fight off the virus if it does enter your body, but washing your hands provides a bit of extra protection. Be sure you don't use antibacterial soap for this. Antibacterial soaps are completely unnecessary and they cause far more harm than good.

Chapter 4

RESTORE YOUR SOUL

The Great Commandment/Generations

When it comes to restoring our soul, we need to uproot and replace old mindsets that may have been stuck in our family bloodlines for generations before us. In our generation, there is increasing visibility of the separation from God, His word, and His love; as well as the separation from others and us.

The great commandment reads in Matthew 22:36-40, "Jesus said unto him, you shall love the Lord your God with all your heart, and with all your soul, and with all your mind. This is the first and great commandment. And the second is like unto it, you shall love your neighbor as yourself. On these two commandments hang all the law and the prophets." So, what does that look like? In practice, how do you love the Lord your God with all of your heart, with your entire mind and with all your soul? Sometimes that is hard to do when you are separated from God due to someone, possibly an earthly father or mother, injuring you. This is where it becomes so important that we know the Father's love and work through any voids or wounds in that relationship.

The Word says in John 3:16, "For God so loved the world, that he gave his only begotten Son, that whosoever believes in him should not perish, but have everlasting life." He loved the world so much that He gave His Son and watched Him be beaten and bruised and rejected and scorned of men and crucified, which was one of the worst possible ways to die at that time. He did that, so that He could get a hold of your heart and mine, and bring us to Himself. And it also says in 1 John 4:16, "And we have known and believed the love that God has for us. God is love; and he that dwells in love dwells in God, and God in him."

God is love! He comes to us reshaping ourselves in Christ, so that these aren't just words that we read, but a real and tangible experience. The reference "to know" refers to a level of intimacy, or "in-to-him-I-see." I have intimacy with the Lord. To develop that kind of intimacy requires day-to-day building and planting trust seed-by-seed. It means encountering Him through the diligence and discipline of sacred rhythms so that you become free from any negative example of fatherhood that you may have had with your earthly father or whoever that parental figure was that may have failed you.

When I teach classes, I often ask the crowd how many of their fathers were absent from their life as a child. Roughly 80% would raise their hand in a typical class. I find that very revealing both of our nation and our church! I believe that the government of God is family.

We have gotten away from using the family as the standard for the plumb line, because generation after generation, there has been a shift and slowly but surely, Satan has made his way in there and impacted the family. He has caused both fathers and mothers to become absent either physically or emotionally from their children. Since our parents are supposed to be a godly representation of the father, when this happens, the children then begin to see God in whatever lenses has been handed to them. If their father was emotionally distant, they may struggle with feeling distant from God. If their father was abusive, they will see God as a punisher. We have to move through and beyond that paradigm. Thus, the importance of being re-parented by the Father.

The second commandment is to "love your neighbor as yourself." If you cannot love yourself well, it is going to be very hard to love another person. A good way to tell if you love yourself is to take inventory on how you talk to yourself. What is your inner dialogue that no one else hears but yourself? Do you believe that you were created in the image of God? When you stand in front of the mirror, can you look at yourself and say that you are fearfully and wonderfully made?

Once you are able to love yourself, it then becomes easier to love others. You'll be able to recognize that God-shaped hole that every one of us has at some point. You'll no longer be inclined to see other people's flaws, but you'll be included to find the gold in each person. You will embrace who you are in Him and can then go and love others the same way, even when you are not inclined to...even when they are not being lovable.

Generations

History is important. Globally, as well as individually, history is important because it reveals patterns and reasons for what is present. When I take a history on a patient, I take a physical history of what has occurred in their body and a history of life events at five-year intervals starting at age 5 and all the way up to the present. The reason I do that is because I want to know all about the great things that you can recall that have blessed your life. I also want to know all the traumatic things that you need or needed to work through. It provides a small snapshot of how the individual has dealt with life. I then take a spiritual history as well as inventory their sacred rhythms (church attendance, worship practice, etc). This gives me insight to their restoration process.

In the physical history, I do a review of body systems. I ask my patients to tell me about their relationship with their mom and dad. I even ask about grandparents and children. I look at that because, in medicine, an individual can be predisposed to diseases that were passed from family. We assess that to see where we may need pinpoint where you might be more likely to have medical problems. It also allows you to see the parts of you, both physically and in your personality, where you may be more similar to your father or mother. So when the patient history is reviewed from the whole perspective of the body, soul and spirit as well as from a generational vantage point, it highlights areas to direct and encourage an individual in the directions where they need to go.

As I discussed earlier, we hear things from three different sources. God, ourselves, and the enemy. The in-depth health history also allows me to see if you may have been passed down toxic thought patterns from your parents. We can then break down unhealthy generational thought patterns and step into all that we are called to be in Jesus.

Remember Who You Are

The importance of identity cannot be underestimated in the context of our soul. So much of our personality, our dreams, callings, and desires derive from our soul. As such, it is important to keep in front of us the truth of our identity.

The following reading is a truth that has sustained me over the years and I want to offer it to you to review, meditate, recite and otherwise internalize such that your soul will not be found wanting and caught unaware!

Who I Am In Christ

I AM ACCEPTED..

John 1:12 I am God's child.
John 15:15 As a disciple, I am a friend of Jesus Christ.
Romans 5:1 I have been justified (declared righteous).
1 Corinthians 6:17 I am united with the Lord, and I am one with Him in spirit.
1 Corinthians 6:19-20 I have been bought with a price and I belong to God.
1 Corinthians 12:27 I am a member of Christ's body.
Ephesians 1:3-8 I have been chosen by God and adopted as His child.
Colossians 1:13-14 I have been redeemed and forgiven of all my sins.
Colossians 2:9-10 I am complete in Christ.
Hebrews 4:14-16 I have direct access to the throne of grace through Jesus Christ.

I AM SECURE.

Romans 8:1-2 I am free from condemnation.
Romans 8:28 I am assured that God works for my good in all circumstances.
Romans 8:31-39 I am free from any condemnation brought

against me and I cannot be separated from the love of God.
2 Corinthians 1:21-22 I have been established, anointed and sealed by God.
Colossians 3:1-4 I am hidden with Christ in God.
Philippians 1:6 I am confident that God will complete the good work He started in me.
Philippians 3:20 I am a citizen of heaven.
2 Timothy 1:7 I have not been given a spirit of fear but of power, love and a sound mind.
1 John 5:18 I am born of God and the evil one cannot touch me.

I AM SIGNIFICANT.
John 15:5 I am a branch of Jesus Christ, the true vine, and a channel of His life.
John 15:16 I have been chosen and appointed to bear fruit.
1 Corinthians 3:16 I am God's temple.
2 Corinthians 5:17-21 I am a minister of reconciliation for God.
Ephesians 2:6 I am seated with Jesus Christ in the heavenly realm.
Ephesians 2:10 I am God's workmanship.
Ephesians 3:12 I may approach God with freedom and confidence.
Philippians 4:13 I can do all things through Christ, who strengthens me.

By Neil Anderson
Who I am in Christ Freedom In Christ Ministries, Dr Neil T Anderson, www.ficm.org

How Sin Affects Your Being

Sin plays such a driving role in the dis-ease of our health. Since we are a being made if spirit, soul, and body, sin has it's destructive affects on every part of us. It is important that we look into the different pathways that lead us into destruction. The Bible clearly shows us the effects of sin in James 1:12-15:

"Blessed [happy, spiritually prosperous, favored by God] is the man who is steadfast under trial and perseveres when tempted; for when he has passed the test and been approved, he will receive the [victor's] crown of life which the Lord has promised to those who love Him. Let no one say when he is tempted, "I am being tempted by God" [for temptation does not originate from God, but from our own flaws]; for God cannot be tempted by [what is] evil, and He Himself tempts no one. But each one is tempted when he is dragged away, enticed and baited [to commit sin] by his own [worldly] desire (lust, passion). Then when the illicit desire has conceived, it gives birth to sin; and when sin has run its course, it gives birth to death."

James clearly lays out the steps to sin and he says that it begins with temptation, which is the desire to do something wrong. Now, temptation itself is not sin! After all, Jesus himself was faced with temptation. It only becomes sin when were act upon that temptation. When you move into temptation, there is often a little voice inside of you that says warns you that what you are about to do it wrong. Some people call that voice a conscience, however I believe that little voice is the Holy Spirit.

James goes on to say, "But every person is tempted when he is drawn away." You're being caused to move in a particular direction, as though a force is drawing you in the opposite direction. Ideally, we should be trained in a God-consciousness that is so high that you can recognize the temptation, resist it, and move away from the temptation and towards God.

Another step is to be enticed, which is to be attracted or to be tempted by something offering pleasure or an advantage. Enticement comes when something appeals to you. It presents a false "award" for you. For example, if you see someone fishing, they throw the bait into the water to allure the fish. The fish becomes drawn to the bait and follows this lure around. Say, for example that you are the fish in this scenario. You follow that bait around and eventually bite, however once you get caught on the hook, you'll quickly realize that the lure rips inside of you and ends up hurting, or even killing you! Sometimes, you'll find that our personal flesh desires sin so much that we lie to ourselves and convince ourselves that we are ok with being hooked, ripped at, and torn apart. However, once you want to get free, you will find that the hook has cut so deeply, it takes time to fully remove. Enticement carries that power.

Sin comes from your own natural desires. Since we were born into a fallen world, we were born as sinners. Psalm 51:5 says, "Surely I was sinful at birth, sinful from the time my mother conceived me."[18] However, we are not lost for hope! Thankfully, God is a God of grace and has given us the ability to be able to manage ourselves and our desires.

Again, I cannot stress enough that have a desire for something does not constitute for sin. It only becomes sin when we hand our power over to our desires. What has been seen in the spirit realm now becomes a physical manifestation. When sin is born, it comes forth

18 NIV Version

and it brings forth death. Referring back to the fish analogy, the fish is pulled up out of the water, out of its own natural environment, where it is unable to breath or survive. This is like sin because when sin is fully mature, it brings forth death. That fish ends up dying.

Of course, every one has encountered temptation and given in. Everybody makes mistakes and there is no condemnation in Christ! However, the idea is to be self-aware of what our temptations are and to be alert to when we notice ourselves being drawn to it. There is absolutely no doubt about it that sin will come to tempt you. It comes in the forms of addictions, bitterness, anger, resentment, and rejection. Thus, it is imperative to train yourself to live with a strong God-consciousness. To live in this place takes time. As I've said before, it is seed by seed, row by row, that is how you make your garden grow!

I have found that God-consciousness is the best, most effective way to avoid being caught up in sin. When we develop a God-consciousness that is strong and compelling within us, we stand up to the test and we receive the crown of life. We can chase after the things of God and we become an overcomer.

Ultimately, we overcome sin by knowing the father's love. Restoration comes as we reconnect with the Father who knows every part of us! His love is the source of our restoration. The most powerful tool I've found to get straight to the heart of His love where you will find true acceptance and restoration. I've included a poem that has minister to me greatly over the years. I recommend that you copy this and read it over yourself morning and night if you can!

THE FATHER'S LOVE LETTER

The Father's Love Letter- 1999 Father Heart Communications. www.FathersLoveLetter.com/media-center.html

Dear child,
You may not know me, but I know everything about you. Psalm 139:1
I know when you sit down and when you rise up. Psalm 139:2
I am familiar with all your ways. Psalm 139:3
Even the very hairs on your head are numbered. Matthew 10:29-31
For you were made in my image. Genesis 1:27
In me, you live and move and have your being. Acts 17:28
For you are my offspring. Acts 17:28
I knew you even before you were conceived. Jeremiah 1:4-5
I chose you when I planned creation. Ephesians 1:11-12
You were not a mistake, for all your days are written in my book. Psalm 139:15-16
I determined the exact time of your birth and where you would live. Acts 17:26
You are fearfully and wonderfully made. Psalm 139:14
I knit you together in your mother's womb. Psalm 139:13
And brought you forth on the day you were born. Psalm 71:6
Those who don't know me have misrepresented me. John 8:41-44
I am not distant and angry, but am the complete expression of love. 1 John 4:16
And it is my desire to lavish my love on you. 1 John 3:1
Simply because you are my child and I am Your Father. 1 John 3:1
I offer you more than your earthly father ever could. Matthew 7:11
For I am your perfect father. Matthew 5:48
Every good gift that you receive comes from my hand. James 1:17
For I am your provider and I meet all your needs. Matthew 6:31-33

My plan for your future has always been filled with hope. Jeremiah 29:11
Because I love you with an everlasting love. Jeremiah 31:3
My thoughts toward you are countless as the sand on the seashore. Psalms 139:17-18
And I rejoice over you with singing. Zephaniah 3:17
I will never stop doing well to you. Jeremiah 32:40
For you are my treasured possession. Exodus 19:5
I desire to establish you with all my heart and all my soul. Jeremiah 32:41
And I want to show you great and marvelous things. Jeremiah 33:3
If you seek me with all of his heart, you will find me. Deuteronomy 4:29
Delight in me and I will give you the desires of your heart. Psalm 37:4
For it is I who gave you those desires. Philippians 2:13
I am able to do more for you than you could possibly imagine. Ephesians 3:20
For I am your greatest encourager. 2 Thessalonians 2:16-17
I am also the Father who comforts you in all your troubles. 2 Corinthians 1:3-4
When you are brokenhearted, I am close to you. Psalm 34:18
As a shepherd carries a lamb, I have carried you close to my heart. Isaiah 40:11
One day I will wipe away every tear from your eyes. Revelation 21:3-4
And I'll take away all the pain you has suffered on this earth. Revelation 21:3-4
I am Your Father, and I love you even as I love my son, Jesus. John 17:23
For in Jesus, my love for you is revealed. John 17:26
He is the exact representation of my being. Hebrews 1:3

He came to demonstrate that I am for you, not against you. Romans 8:31
And to tell you that I am not counting your sins. 2 Corinthians 5:18-19
Jesus died so that you and I could be reconciled. 2 Corinthians 5:18-19
His death was the ultimate expression of my love for you. 1 John 4:10
I gave up everything I loved that I might gain your love. Romans 8:31-32
If you receive the gift of my son Jesus, You receive me. 1 John 2:23
And nothing will ever separate you from my love again. Romans 8:38-39
Come home and I'll throw the biggest party heaven has ever seen. Luke 15:7
I have always been Father, and will always be Father. Ephesians 3:14-15
My question is…will you be my child? John 1:12-13
I am waiting for you. Luke 15:11-32

Love, your father
Almighty God

Chapter 5

RESTORE YOUR SPIRIT

Meditating on God's Word

Joshua 1:8 says, "Keep this Book of the Law always on your lips; meditate on it day and night, so that you may be careful to do everything written in it. Then you will be prosperous and successful." That's a powerful statement! So what does it look like to meditate on the word of God? Simply put, it means to read the word of God! There is life to be found on each and every page in the Bible and it brings a refreshing and peace over your soul that is unlike any other.

About 20 years ago, an amazing woman by the name of Rose became my spiritual mother and she began to disciple me. She is the type of mother that always takes my phone call no matter the time of day or night. When I was being disciple by her, it was a very simple program she used and it helped me grow in the Lord immensely. I never thought then that I would be where I am today. Bless the Lord, oh my soul! One thing Rose encouraged me to do was to immerse myself in the Word of God daily! Whenever I would call her with a problem that I needed clarity with she would always ask first, "Johnnett, have you been in the word for 5 minutes today?" It got to the point where I knew to spend at least five minutes in the Word of God before calling her with whatever problem I was facing. Even a short five minutes is often times enough to help calm my spirit and bring me back to a place of alignment with God.

One of my favorite scriptures is Psalm 119:11. I particularly love The Passion Translation of this Psalm. Verse 11 says, "I consider your word to be my greatest treasure. I memorize them and write them on my heart to keep me from committing sin treasons against You."

The word of God should be our greatest treasure! Therefore, the words of God are so important to our lives. We are to write them on the tablets of our heart in order that we can walk in righteousness and not sin against the Lord. I often believe that some of the mistakes people make in their lives could have been avoided if they had only been meditating in the Word of God more. When we find ourselves spending time in the Bible, we encounter Jesus. When we encounter Jesus, we can't help but fall in love with Him. When you love a person, you want to avoid doing anything that would bring pain to their heart.

It is without a doubt the most beautiful covenantal piece of weaponry that we have! The word of God has to be stored in our hearts to be able to obtain the victory!

Hebrews 4: 12 "For the word of God is alive and active. Sharper than any double-edged sword, it penetrates even to dividing soul and spirit, joints and marrow; it judges the thoughts and attitudes of the heart." From a medical standpoint, the marrow is where the immune system is housed! This tells me that the Word of God has the power to change us both spiritually and physically. It affects your spirit, soul and body. It even affects your thoughts and the intentions of your heart. That is how powerful the word of God is! It's a sword that needs to be hidden in our hearts for our defense and our protection.

God can work miraculously and some believers have an encounter with God and gain an immediate knowledge of His word. In my life and walk however, I have had to learn it all by reading it, re-reading it and reading it again! In college, I had a friend whom I'd attend church with, who would say things like, "I read the bible once." Even as a new Christian, I would think "are you kidding me?" He needed to talk to Rose, my mentor, who would ask if I had read for at least 5 minutes that day! His Word is new each day with mysteries to reveal. There are many, including Bill Johnson who I see as my spiritual father, who have immersed themselves in the Word on a daily basis. His revelation and wisdom that God gives him is truly amazing. My desire is to be able to walk in the wisdom of God so that I can help others to receive wisdom to change their future.

The Word of God is an absolute key piece of your spiritual armor, which is identified in Ephesians 6. Meditating on God's word is vitally important to restoring your spirit. You meditate on this so that it is hidden in your heart, so that you won't sin against the Lord, so that it can go before you and prepare the way for others and to reconcile others back. And again, it is powerful and sharper than any two-edged sword.

Declaration of the Word of God

The declaration of the word of God is another essential sacred rhythm. A declaration is defined as "the formal announcement of the beginning of a state or condition."[19]

19 http://www.dictionary.com/browse/declaration

Job 22:28 says, "You will also decree a thing, then it will be established." The word for decree in Hebrew is "gazar" and it means to cut off, to pass no longer, to declare the future. There is a line of separation when you "decree" a thing. This is also why it is so important to watch your words and your speech.

In Luke 6:35 it says, " a good man, out of the good treasure of his heart, brings forth what is good. And an evil man, out of the evil treasure of his heart, brings forth that which is evil. For out of the abundance of the heart, the mouth speaks." What we speak, reveals the nature of our heart. If we our speech is negative and slanderous, it reveals that we have deep resentment or bitterness in our hearts. If our speech is uplifting and promising, it reveals that we have joy and peace in our hearts. The beauty of this is that if you find that your speech is negative, you have the opportunity to change it! This ties directly into meditating on the Word of God. If we mediate on the Word of God, our speech should begin to reflect it. When you are speaking good things, it renews you. As it says in Isaiah, your youth is renewed! When you are speaking and moving from a positive perspective or heart set or heart posture, and not a negative heart posture, you bring forth positive things into your life. Psalm 103:5 says, "You satisfy my mouth with good things. You super-charge my life so that I soar again, like flying eagles in the sky."[20] The word of God satisfies our mouth and brings satisfaction to our heart.

Earlier in the book, we talked about how we have learned behaviors and mindsets that are developed through life experiences. You have a history that your heart knows very well. It knows it both generationally and figuratively from your youth to your present day. Because of this, that beautiful heart of every believer needs to be renewed. It gets to have the power to change as you draw and

20 The Passion Translation

hunger for the God-consciousness to be present in your life. You will begin to find freedom from the heavy burdens that your heart carried. You will find freedom from being a victim. The idea is to renew yourself and to know God's word and to have it hidden in your heart, speaking out what is positive and good. What you speak, you will become. So if you want to be free, start declaring over yourself Bible verses about freedom!

I have a book called, *Decree a Thing and it Shall Be Established* by Patricia King. I use it to declare life changing truths over my life, my husband's life, and the lives of my children. When I first began making declarations, I didn't necessarily believe them. However, over time the words I spoke began to create a new groove in my brain patterns and I soon began to truly believe what I was saying! His word is my truth, my foundation, and my rock! By using declarations of the word and promises over my life, I am cutting off the sinful part of my past and declaring that I agree with the word. I am declaring that I am favored of the Lord and that I have victory! I am the head and not the tail, every cell in my body is healthy, I am full of life! I didn't get any of that just because I rested my head on top of the word of God.

In Exodus 17:14, we learn about the battle of Amalech. It says, "Then Moses said to Joshua, write this in a book as a memorial, and recite it to Joshua, that I will utterly blot out the memory of the Amalech from under the heavens." We see that Joshua won against Amalech and Moses was telling Joshua to write the victory in a book for remembrance. "Recite" means to repeat aloud and from memory. The Lord is instructing Joshua to write it down as a memorial and then to recite it. You repeat it from memory and say it out loud. The desire would be for you to have your victories in a book or on a wall in your house to keep on hand so you can always feast on His goodness and faithfulness. God wants us to recite those things for a reason! When we are going through bad times, we can recite and remember all the times that God has come through for us.

I keep a have a journal where I have written down the prophecies that were spoken over me as well as answered prayers that have happened in my life, so that they are a memorial to the Lord and anyone that finds them. I can't take credit for this idea, however. It was taken from Bill Johnson's book, *Strengthen Yourself in the Lord.*

So, you need to declare the word of God over your life! Recite it and repeat it so that it gets down to your heart. Your heart has to be postured with the Word of God so that out of the abundance of your heart, your mouth speaks. As you grow in God and get free from sin and brokenness, you will begin to live in victory.

Praying In The Spirit

One of my favorite ways to bring restoration to my spirit is by speaking in tongues. This is an area where religion has skewed the value and power of this gift and many Christians are entirely unfamiliar or misinformed concerning its use, practice, and power. Some denominations even say that it is evil, wicked, and demonic. Others say that it isn't for today or that it has died away. It can be extremely controversial until you experience the richness and power it brings. I have been praying in tongues for years and I know the value and power of this practice in my own life.

God's word says in 1 Corinthians 14:1, "Follow after charity and desire the spiritual gifts, but rather that you may prophesy. For he that speaks in an unknown tongue speaks not unto men but unto God, for no man understands him. How be it in the spirit he speaks mysteries." Speaking in tongues is a way that our spirits commune and communicate with God. When we speak in an unknown tongue, we speak not to communicate to man, but to God.

People often forget to pray. I was once taking a class and I was challenged to pray in the spirit for 30 minutes everyday. I decided to take on the challenge and I have found it to be a wellspring of life for me. I set a timer and timed myself praying in the spirit for 30 minutes every day until it became a habit and part of the rhythm of my day. It is one more beautiful sacred rhythm that brings freedom for myself and it keeps me in the love of God. In my prayer time, my spirit searches for the mercies of the Lord so that I can give that compassion out to others. I find it very helpful also, in stressful situations because it helps align my spirit with God's. The Lord is faithful to give me insight while praying in the spirit.

I encourage you to practice it. Begin with just five minutes every day and grow to 30 minutes or more if you can! Praying in tongues brings you to a place of revelation and empowerment! God will reveal Himself through those who will invest themselves in Him. A pastor at Bethel Church once told me about how he once prayed in the spirit for 24 hours, which gave him great insight and revelation for people to build them up in love or to lay hands on the sick, or to disciple. It is a worthy, worthy gift and sacred rhythm!

Church and Fellowship

Surround yourself with people who make you hungry for life, touch your heart and nourish your soul!

The sacred rhythm of participation in the body of Christ is another vital aspect of our spiritual health and life. In an increasingly "cyber-society," it is easy to justify virtual participation in church. While that may carry some value, it misses the mark and is a poor substitute for live fellowship and participation with others in the body of Christ.

Let's first look at what the Word says about fellowship. In 1 John 1:3 we read, "That which we have seen and heard declare we unto you, that you also may have fellowship with us: and truly our fellowship is with the Father, and with his Son Jesus Christ." So while we are having fellowship with the church, we also fellowship with God the Father, the Son, and the Holy Spirit.

1 John 1:7 says, "But if we walk in the light, as he is in the light, we have fellowship one with another, and the blood of Jesus Christ his Son cleanses us from all sin." Here we find that there is victory in our fellowship with one another because the blood of Jesus cleanses us from all sin. So the fellowship brings the light of the Lord into our lives. Light is essential to life. Fellowship brings us together and we become like-minded and enjoy the blessings of unity in life.

The Word makes it clear what we are called to community. Jesus himself had community here on earth and committed himself to spending time with others. There are both spiritual and physical benefits to community and fellowship. Let's look briefly at what happens in our body when we fellowship. When you are with people, oxytocin is released into your brain. Oxytocin reduces stress, which in turn lowers cortisol and can then boost the immune system. Not only does community bring life in our spirits, but it has direct physical and psychological impact on us as well! So let's all get to church and be together to release our love to the Lord. Surround yourself with people who make you hungry for life, touch your heart, and nourish your soul!

Section 2

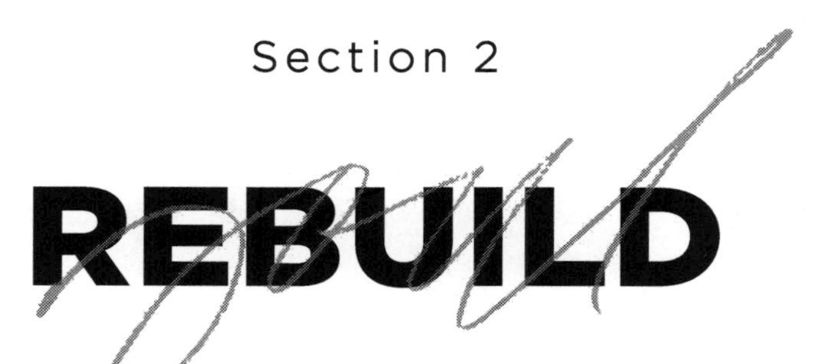

REBUILD

"I will restore the fortunes of my people Israel, and they shall rebuild the ruined cities and inhabit them; they shall plant vineyards and drink their wine, and they shall make gardens and eat their fruit."

Amos 9:14 ESV

//

Once we have restored the foundation of our life, we are given the chance to rebuild and recreate ourselves. We walked through what it looks like to bring restoration to the broken parts of your body, soul, and spirit. Now, let's dive into what it looks like to rebuild.

Chapter 6

REBUILD YOUR BODY

Exercise

Ahhh, exercise. It's the eight-letter word that nobody likes to talk about and yet all of us need to do it! When talking about exercise, I like to break it down into three categories. The first would be cardio where you increase your heart rate. The second would be strength training, which involves weights or some type of resistance to help build muscles. The third is one I particularly love and that is stretching! Many people overlook stretching but it is a highly effective and needed workout for our bodies!

Cardio

By definition, cardio exercise is a brisk physical activity that requires the heart and lungs to work harder to meet the body's increased oxygen demand. Aerobic exercise promotes the circulation of oxygen through the blood. The key word here is oxygen. We all know that our bodies need oxygen to survive. Without oxygen being replenished in our bodies, unhealthy or weak cells lose their natural immunity and are become more at risk to viruses, which leads to all kinds of serious health problems.

It's important to note that aerobic exercise needs to be at an intensity that forces the heart and lungs to work harder and yet low enough intensity to facilitate adequate oxygen transfer to the muscle cells so that there isn't a buildup of lactic acid. Another way of looking at aerobic exercise is that it involves repetitive movement of large muscle groups (such as your arms, legs, and hips) with all of the needed energy supplied by the oxygen you breathe. When you're aerobically fit, your body takes in and utilizes oxygen more efficiently - to sustain the repetitive muscle movement. Benefits of cardio and aerobic activities include:

/ Improved heart and lung function
/ Lower heart rate and blood pressure
/ Increased blood supply to muscles and improved ability to use oxygen
/ Increased HDL cholesterol (the good cholesterol)
/ Decreased triglycerides
/ Reduced body fat and improved weight control
/ Improved glucose tolerance and reduced insulin resistance
/ Enhanced immune function, which means
    Increased resistance to viral and bacterial infection
    Increased resistance to cancer
/ Lowered blood sugar levels and reduced risk of diabetes
/ Longer life expectancy

When many people think of cardio, they imagine themselves having to slave away miles on a treadmill. However, there is a whole world of aerobic exercise to choose from! Choose one or two that you enjoy and can easily pursue.

/ Running or jogging
/ Swimming
/ Biking
/ Rowing
/ Jumping Rope
/ Speed Walking
/ Elliptical Trainers
/ Stair Steppers

Interval Training

Interval training is another form of aerobic exercise with periods of high intensity activity followed by periods of lower intensity. For example, if you do a running interval workout, you would run at your fastest pace for 20-30 seconds, followed by a rest interval of 30-40 seconds where you walk or lightly jog. You repeat for 8-20 minutes. Interval training has been shown to burn more fat than typical, steady aerobic workouts do.

Strength Training

Strength training involves the use of weights or some other form of resistance to build muscle and increase strength. Its benefits include:

/ Increased muscle strength
/ Increased tendon and ligament strength
/ Reduced body fat and increased muscle mass
/ Better balance
/ Lower blood cholesterol
/ Improved glucose tolerance and insulin sensitivity

Contrary to popular opinion, strength training is not just for young people or for men! Studies have shown that people in their 70's and 80's can increase their strength by up to 180% in a matter of a few weeks! Again, as with aerobics, there is a world of choices when it comes to strength training workouts, which include:

/ Free Weights
/ Weight Machines
/ Resistance Training machines
/ Pilates Equipment
/ Body Weight Exercise
/ Any and all can work. Choose one that works for you and that you can do easily and are willing to do regularly.

It's worth noting that weight training is the best way to burn calories fast! A pound of muscle burns up to nine times the calories of a pound of fat. In other words, strength training increases your resting metabolic rate, which is the number of calories you burn while sleeping or sitting. The reason for this is because muscle is considered active tissue. Meaning it requires a lot of energy just to maintain itself. In fact, every pound of new muscle you add to your body will burn about 60 calories per day! Adding just 10 pounds of muscle to your body could burn off 60 pounds of fat over the next year, even while you are sleeping!

Stretching

The third, and my heart's personal favorite, is stretching! It is the booster, expander, and lengthener of muscles while expanding your body's abilities for movement. Sadly, it gets only lip service paid to it than actual practice. Stretching is crucial to good health. The usual benefits include:

/ Reduced muscle tension
/ Injury prevention
/ Increased range of movement in the joints
/ Enhanced muscular coordination
/ Increased circulation of the blood to various parts of the body
/ Increased energy levels (resulting from increased circulation)

Think for a moment about what the opposite of stretching is. It's tightness and restriction! Tightness and constriction means reduced blood flow to the muscle and soft tissue, a reduced supply of nutrients to the area of tension, and reduced removal of metabolic waste from those areas. Areas that are tense and constricted are then breeding grounds for illness and organ dysfunction. Now tie in the whole concept of traditional Chinese medicine, which says that all disease results from restrictions in the flow of energy in the body because it creates imbalance. You can see that stretching is not just an issue of feeling good, it is essential for maintaining optimum health.

If nothing else, just do 5-10 minutes of simple stretching after your daily exercise routine as part of your cool down time.

jonbarron.org/athletic-performance/need-exercise

Chiropractic Care Benefits

As you may have considered since I am a chiropractor is that I am passionate about chiropractic work! I have been a witness to the miraculous benefits that have come from good, chiropractic care. I've always been drawn to health and wellness and I found myself as a young girl in being drawn by chiropractic care. I eventually studied it in college and began my journey as a chiropractor at the age of 28.

My reason for choosing chiropractic care is because it benefits the entire body as a whole! Most people think chiropractic care us just for your neck or back, and the occasional headache. While we do address those, our main focus is not just relieving pain but encouraging the body to be able to heal itself.

Chiropractic care allows for the body to be as stress-free as possible. While many people live on a stress roller coaster, people who stay well adjusted find that their bodies are able to manage stress more efficiently. I'd have to say that the best application for chiropractic care in our lives is for preventative maintenance. I like to compare it to taking care of a garden. We can't just prepare the soil and wait for flowers to bloom and for plants to grow. We have to be the ones to plant the seeds and be diligent about making sure it gets its daily water and adequate sunshine. We must be sure to remove the weeds that may try to come in to destroy what we've planted. The same is true for our bodies. We can't see a chiropractor one time and expect to live a pain-free life. Our goal is to keep the body in good working order and we do that by keeping the spine well adjusted. By doing this, nerve interferences are removed from the body and this keeps communication lines between organs and muscles groups in tact.

Chiropractic care is so much more than just the readjustment of bones and muscles. It actually helps alleviate pain, stimulate blood movement, supports your immune system, and pushes oxygen into your body! Benefits include:

/ Reduced back pain
/ Headache relief
/ Reduced ear infections
/ Reduced neck pain
/ Relief from scoliosis
/ Asthma relief
/ Lowered blood pressure
/ Promotes healthy pregnancy

draxe.com/10-researched-benefits-chiropractic-adjustments/

Chiropractic care has also been shown to help lessen the effects of oxidative stress on our bodies. Oxidative stress happens when there are not enough antioxidants in our bodies to help fight off free radicals. World renowned chiropractor Dr. Christopher Kent explained: "Oxidative stress, metabolically generating free radicals, is now a broadly accepted theory of how we age and develop disease

Going through life, we experience physical, chemical and emotional stress. These stresses affect the function of the nervous system. We hypothesized that these disturbances in nerve function could affect oxidative stress and DNA repair on a cellular level. Chiropractic care appears to improve the ability of the body to adapt to stress," concluded Kent.[21] Amazing, what Dr. Kent had to say. But, I have been a witness to the miraculous benefits that have come from good, chiropractic care.

www.ncbi.nlm.nih.gov/pmc/articles/PMC2686395/
http://www.palmer.edu/about-us/what-is-chiropractic/

Cleanses

I found this to be truly notable those many many years ago
"Health begins in the GI tract." –Hippocrates

Your intestinal tract is the source of all nutrient access to your body. If it isn't working properly, you have two major problems. First, you have a hard time digesting food and breaking it down sufficiently so that your body can use it. Even if you can digest it properly, if the intestinal wall is covered with hardened mucous and/or colonies of hostile bacteria, you'll end up absorbing only a fraction of the nutritional value of the food you eat!

In addition, the colon is the main elimination channel of the body. It is the means by which we eliminate the toxic waste of the digestive process, including massive amounts of E. coli bacteria. If that waste hangs around longer than necessary, its impact on the body is profound. We've already discussed how waste from the

21 https://draxe.com/your-chiropractor-could-be-your-newest-antioxidant/

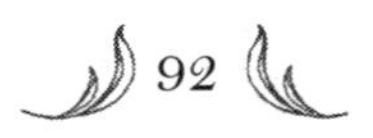

lymph system passes out through the colon along with waste from the liver. The liver filters out dangerous drug residues, poisons, and excess cholesterol from the blood and passes them out of the body through the colon via the bile duct and gallbladder. Plug the colon and everything backs up. The net result is sickness and disease. The important point to remember here is that you can't even begin to cleanse and repair the other systems in the body until you clean out the colon so that the toxic material will have a path out of the body.

Physically, the colon is not designed to store large amounts of old fecal matter. If you have pounds of extra garbage in there, there's only one thing that can happen; the colon must distend and expand. This causes the walls of the colon to thin out (like blowing up a balloon more and more). As the walls extend out, they press on and compress other organs in the abdominal cavity. Old fecal matter is an ideal breeding ground for harmful bacteria and dangerous parasites.

A good cleanse must serve to do the following:

/ Remove all old fecal matter and waste from the colon (to clear the drain, if you will).
/ Help remove all of the heavy metals and drug residues that have accumulated in the body and tissue of the intestinal wall as a result of having your drain plugged.
/ Strengthen the colon muscle so that it works again.
/ Repair any damage, such as herniation (diverticula) and inflammations of the colon and small intestine.
/ Eliminate the presence of polyps and other abnormal growths that have been allowed to flourish because of an unhealthy intestinal environment.
/ Rebuild and replenish the various "friendly" bacteria cultures

that ideally should line virtually every square inch of the tract--again, from mouth to anus, excluding the stomach.

Is it any wonder with the following diseases that the need is significant for a good GI cleanse? There are many choices available. But don't become a statistic and do nothing and end up with one of the top GI disorders in the US.

The most prevalent digestive diseases include:

/ Constipation and the attendant symptoms of self-toxification
/ Diverticular disease (herniations of the colon)
/ Polyps
/ Hemorrhoids
/ Irritable bowel syndrome
/ Ulcerative colitis
/ Crohn's disease
/ Colorectal cancer

jonbarron.org/topic/intestinal-detoxification-rebuilding

There are so many choices out there. One of my favorites is following *The Maker's Diet* by Dr. Jordan Rubin who direct and utilizes wonderful and powerful whole foods and lifestyle changes. There are many out there as I mentioned before so do your research and find one that's right for you.

Chapter 7

REBUILD YOUR SOUL

Taking Every Thought Captive

"Diseases follow thought lines not blood lines."
Abraham Hicks

It is vital for our health that we learn to take our thoughts captive. We are faced with thousands of thoughts a day and they have the ability to make or break us! When we fail to take our thoughts captive, we can go into captivity and we get stuck in a cage with the cage door wide open. Isaiah 5:13 says, "Therefore my people have gone into captivity, because they have no knowledge: and their honorable men are famished, and their multitude dried up with thirst." We have recieved Jesus and all the gifts he bestowed upon us, yet we haven't yet practiced this strategy.

We must take every thought captive to win the war! But first, let's take a look at your thoughts. You have about 160,000 thoughts per day. That breaks down to 120 thoughts per minute! Even on your best day, it's about 86,000 thoughts a day that you can probably successfully hold captive, which depends on your wavelengths (that is how able your brain is to even register each thought fully). At your highest max, you can manage about 1.3 thoughts per second. That is a lot of thoughts to hold captive! Paul would not have written this to the Corinthians if we didn't have the ability to hold our thoughts captive, right? To take a thought, mental picture, opinion, judgment, or anticipation captive, we have to tear down the barriers of that thought. Thankfully, the Lord has given us instruction on how to do that.

2 Corinthians 10:3-6 says, " The world is unprincipled. It's "dog-eat-dog" out there! The world doesn't fight fair. But we don't live or fight our battles that way—never have and never will. The tools of our trade aren't for marketing or manipulation, but they are for demolishing that entire massively corrupt culture. We use our powerful God-tools for smashing warped philosophies, tearing down barriers erected against the truth of God, fitting every loose thought and emotion and impulse into the structure of life shaped by Christ. Our tools are ready at hand for clearing the ground of every obstruction and building lives of obedience into maturity."[22]

It just puts the hammer to the nail. We are not like everyone else in the world. That is not how we wage our war. We wage our war by taking every thought captive. In the New King James it says "For though we walk and live in the flesh we are not carrying out warfare according to the flesh and using mere human weapons, for the weapons of our warfare are not physical weapons of flesh and blood, but they are mighty before God to overthrow and destroy strongholds as we refute arguments, theories, and reasoning. We lead every thought and purpose away captive into obedience of Christ, the anointed one. Being in readiness to punish every insubordinate for his disobedience, when your own submission and obedience as a

22 The Message Translation

church is fully secured and complete."

When we come into who we are in Christ and we continue with the life of the renewed mind and knowing God's word, our battle isn't against flesh and blood. Let me say it again, the battle is not against flesh and blood! It is not the human being that stands there who is warring against us. We have to remove ourselves from the situation and remember that there is a God-shaped hole in every human being.

So, when we come back from whatever conflicts or life situations come before us, we need to come back to this basic principle. Otherwise, you go down the wrong path and you walk around being offended. You have to take your thinking captive and become aware of how you process thoughts. It is imperative because it shifts the position that you would take in building a case against a person, a situation or a political party, a church, a denomination, etc. If you don't do that, you go down the proverbial primrose path. You have to tear down the barriers of thought. You have to rebuild and strengthen the mind of Christ in you so that you can think like the Father and speak like Jesus.

Sin In The Flesh

Romans 8:1-3 says, "*There is* therefore now no condemnation to them which are in Christ Jesus, who walk not after the flesh, but after the Spirit. For the law of the Spirit of life in Christ Jesus hath made me free from the law of sin and death. For what the law could not do, in that it was weak through the flesh, God sending his own Son in the likeness of sinful flesh, and for sin, condemned sin in the flesh."

So what does that mean that God condemned sin in the flesh? Physically, the body does not commit sin. It may be an instrument or weapon that does the sin, but there is no sin in the physical body itself. Sin lies in the will, as in the mind, will and emotions. If you choose sin, you then use your body as a tool to commit the sin, which opens the spiritual floodgates for the remnants of sin to take root inside the physical body.

So now, sin is in the flesh. In Romans 8:11 it says, "But if the Spirit of him that raised up Jesus from the dead dwell in you, he that raised up Christ from the dead shall also quicken your mortal bodies by his Spirit that dwelled in you."

The word "quicken" means to come alive, make alive, or to give life. We are talking about healing life coming to your physical body. How exactly does the Holy Spirit do that? He does this by becoming one with your spirit.

So if you are carnally minded, sin is breaking the law within your body, which is now making you sick or diseased. Let's take the word diseased and make it dis-eased, meaning broken law or wrecked ease, or in other words: ease that has been destroyed. Ease is health and dis-ease is sickness. The body is supposed to dwell in ease and be at a place of homeostasis. Homeostasis is the balanced equilibrium within the body that keeps your temperature at 98.6 and your pulse rate proper. You have vital signs, which include your blood pressure, temperature, vision, hearing, and touch. They all are trying to stay at homeostasis. When that homeostasis is gone, instead of one kind of sickness that happens in the body in mental illness, there are three sicknesses. You are sick in your spirit, soul and body.

The basic sickness is a spiritual sickness. You are spiritually sick if you don't have a relationship with Jesus. If you don't know Jesus, you don't even know what is going on in your members or the parts of your body as referenced in Romans 6-8. I personally believe all sickness is a spiritual sickness. If you were healed in your spirit, your body would be well. Your body would respond to your spirit and ultimately recover.

Based on science, they have developed a branch of medicine called psychoneuroimmunology. The science started in 1865 and has developed since. There was a book written on the wisdom of thinking in 1932. It wasn't until 1975 when Robert Adder actually coined the phrase "psychoneuroimmunology." So to break that word down, "psycho" refers to your thinking. "Neuro" is how it responds to your nervous system and where it goes in your nervous system, which would be your mind will and emotions. "Immunology" is speaking of how it affects your immune system.

Taking it a step further, we are a spirit, we have a soul, and we live in this body. We should have a branch called "pneumo" instead of "psycho", -neuroimmunology. "Pneumo" referring to spirit. Instead of just the mind affecting the nervous system and immune system, the spirit affects the thought life, which in-turn affects the nervous system and immune system.

Here is an example of where I am going with this idea. Galatians 5:16-26 says, "But if you bite and devour one another, take heed that you be not consumed one of another. *This* I say then, Walk in the Spirit, and you shall not fulfill the lust of the flesh. For the flesh lusts against the Spirit, and the Spirit against the flesh: and these are contrary the one to the other: so that you cannot do the things that you would. But if you are led of the Spirit, you are not under the law. Now the works of the flesh are manifest, which are *these*; Adultery, fornication, uncleanness, lasciviousness, Idolatry, witchcraft, hatred, variance, emulations, wrath, strife, seditions, heresies, envyings, murders, drunkenness, revellings, and such like: of the which I tell you before, as I have also told *you* in time past, that they which do such things shall not inherit the kingdom of God. But the fruit of the Spirit is love, joy, peace, longsuffering, gentleness, goodness, faith, Meekness, temperance: against such there is no law. And they that are Christ's have crucified the flesh with the affections and lusts. If we live in the Spirit, let us also walk in the Spirit. Let us not be desirous of vain glory, provoking one another, envying one another."

I'm going to break this down for you in an example. Let's say that I got discouraged and lost all courage. Immediately, my consciousness or my spirit-man becomes downtrodden. The only way to put a man on his feet again is to renew a right spirit within him. We know that discouragement is not a fruit of the Holy Spirit, so we are now allowing another spirit to take root in our hearts. When you are downtrodden, you have to build yourself up in the spirit. You can do this by reading the word and spending time in worship or in prayer. I personally find myself experiencing the fullest renewal when I read the word of God. This process helps renew our mind and will clean house, so to speak, of any other influence that may be trying to make it's home in our body.

Now we have my picture of the 3 circles. We can see the body, the soul, and the spirit. So, when you spirit-man is strong and overcoming, it overcomes the soul, which is transformed by the renewing of your mind, which cascades into your body. The goal is for those three circles to unite and have so much overlap that the spirit (the biggest and most important circle) has been renewed and would literally transform your body. Someone who has been sick in the spirit for quite a while will have likely gotten it down into their soul, which then passed on into their body.

James 4: 7 says, "Submit to God, resist the devil and he will flee from you." This verse instructs us to submit to God our mind, body, and spirit. It is part of the resistance phase. You step into your resistance, stand firm holding true to the Spirit and the Word of God and the devil has no option but to flee from you. He has to obey you because he is under your feet. He is not that strong. You are overcoming and empowering.

My husband and I have incorporated a program called "Pathways to Wholeness" which is a 10 week course created by Restoration Christian Ministry that you attend or observe on line once per week. After session 6, there is a session of ministry, which is just an 8-hour day of worshipping God, declaring His word, and praying over yourself and breaking the bonds of the enemy. The second class is one that teaches about forgiveness, which is so important. When I have taught the "Pathways to Wholeness" curriculum, within the first few days you begin to learn strategies that the enemy has used against you and you begin to gain your own strategies of how to overcome. The goal will always be to think like the Father and to speak like Jesus so that the power of the Holy Ghost can move.

rcministry.org/pathways-to-wholeness/
Pathways to Wholeness Seminar Workbook copyright 2016 Restoration Christian Ministry

There have been many beautiful testimonies that have come out of this course. The first testimony is of a 73 year old gentlemen who had 3rd stage kidney cancer. A beautiful man we will call RS. He came into our course gray and sickly looking. At one point, the spirit of God hit this man and while he was weeping, his gray countenance turned pink and bright within 10 minutes! The Holy Spirit got a hold of him and it was a very beautiful sight to behold. He received healing! God completely transformed his life and on top of it, he was healed of his cancer. His kidney cancer was gone! He went back to the doctors and was cleared of this disease!

Something that Satan can use to keep us from getting victory in our lives could be unforgiveness. There was another woman who came through the class. Here is her testimony:

"First and foremost, Pathways to Wholeness brought me into a more honest and loving relationship with my Father God. The most valuable gift you can give someone you are in relationship with is your time. So I am spending more time with God, in His word and in prayer. My Father is showering me with blessings as I seek Him and what He wants for me and in fact, created me to be. The course taught me about forgiveness in others and myself, which began the healing process of my mind, body, and spirit. I was diagnosed with fibromyalgia and I was living the diagnosis instead of living my life. My life became more abundant as my relationship with God grew with each week of study. I have been set free from the pain I carried from age 3 to age 61. It is never too late to be free. God loves you and you can experience his freedom for yourself."

Those are just two examples of how God moves when we move our lives towards Him and how the body just has to fall in line with the renewed life. They made Him more real in their lives and discovered His countenance and presence, which then aligned with their own spirits. They had the health in their own spirit, which then became evident and manifested in the body.

You and I carry a dominating victorious spirit and my body and your body has to respond to it. However, this only happens when we stand our ground and fight for it. It is my prayer that you will overcome and allow it.

I love to think about Jesus on the Mount of Transfiguration and all the radiant glory that surrounded him. The presence of God was so thick and tangible that the glory just flowed through his flesh until it he glowed and glistened. His clothes were white and his face shone as light. It is that radiant purity of God that my soul just desires so much! Can you imagine being that immersed from the presence of God? I long for my own self to be that "enlightened" and experience the glory of God is coming out of me and going into everyone that I speak to. It is a glorious thing! I believe that our goal should be to become so lost in the presence of God that even our physical body begins to radiant under His glory.

Make The Choice

When God created us, He could have chosen to make us robots who had no ability to make our own decisions. However, because of His grace, He gave us the gift of free will. He created us with the ability to think for ourselves and to make our own choices in life. We get the privilege to make choices about our health. We get to decide if we are going to leave behind the pathways that lead to bitterness and to put our trust back in the Lord. The pathway of bitterness is usually built seed upon seed and likewise, the pathway of trust is also built seed upon seed. So seed by seed and row by row, that is how you make a garden grow. The bitterness pathway and the pathway of trust are the same in this regard. Whichever seed you sow will reap a harvest that produces either life and fruit or death and destruction. It's your choice.

Hebrews 12:15 says, "Exercise foresight *and* be on the watch to look [after one another], to see that no one falls back from *and* fails to secure God's grace (His unmerited favor and spiritual blessing), in order that no root of resentment (rancor, bitterness, or hatred) shoots forth and causes trouble *and* bitter torment, and the many become contaminated *and* defiled by it". As we can see, bitterness is corrosive. It will chew you up and spit you out and literally kill you.

Proverbs 3:5-6 instructs us to, "Trust in the Lord with all your heart and to lean not on your own understanding. In all your ways acknowledge Him and He will direct your path. Do not be wise in your

own eyes, fear the Lord and depart form evil. It will be health to your flesh and strength to your bones. You will get healing to your flesh."

The truth is, our bodies will be renewed with life and be healed while our bones will vibrate with life and be strengthened. There is a renewing that comes from trusting in the Lord. When bitterness is the pathway you choose to go down, then it is not health to your flesh nor is it strength to your bones. It eats you up. It shoots forth and causes trouble and bitter torment deep within you.

Bitterness has a set of brothers that like to associate themselves with it and these brothers are practically looking to harm you permanently. They are like deep roots that penetrate into your body. I personally believe that they are spiritual principalities. In Ephesians, Paul talks about how our struggles are against principalities and powers, not against flesh and blood. When we choose bitterness, it's as if we are clothing ourselves with the armor of disease. Your pieces of armor could look like unforgiveness, resentment, retaliation, anger, hatred, violence, jealousy, and murder.

I have found that when we harbor bitterness in our hearts, we begin to build a case against that person. It could even be towards the Lord or ourselves! The key is to learn and practice forgiveness, which is one of the strongest weapons of spiritual warfare that we carry!n The Lord talks about forgiveness as follows:

For if you forgive men their trespasses, your heavenly Father will also forgive you." Mark 11:25-26

"And when you stand praying, forgive, if you have anything against any: that your Father also who is in heaven may forgive you your trespasses. But if you do not forgive, neither will your Father who is in heaven forgive your trespasses." Matthew 16

"But I say unto you who hear, Love your enemies, do good to them who hate you, Bless them that curse you, and pray for them who despitefully use you." Luke 6:27-28

"Judge not, and you shall not be judged: condemn not, and you shall not be condemned: forgive, and you shall be forgiven." Matthew 18:21-22

"Then came Peter to him, and said, Lord, how often shall my brother sin against me, and I forgive him? till seven times? Jesus said unto him, I say not unto you, Until seven times: but, until seventy times seven." Luke 6:37

Needless to say, when you move into bitterness against someone else, you are sinning against the Lord. What's interesting is that you are also holding yourself hostage. You need to remember that bitterness isn't an emotion. It is a decision. We decide to partner with it and activate it in our lives. Forgiveness is the same. Forgiveness is not an emotion, but a choice. Forgiveness is the path that leads to restoring our hearts before our God the Father, the Lord Jesus, and the Holy Spirit.

Another harmful principality is retaliation. Retaliation and revenge carry the motive to get even with someone. How many times have you been hurt by someone and you find yourself imagining all the ways you could hurt them in return? Our imagination is powerful. In fact, it's so powerful that studies have been shown that the brain cannot differentiate what is real and what is not![23] When we focus on mind on anger and retaliation, our body chemistry begins to change along with it. It is more dangerous than unforgiveness and

23 https://newhopeoutreach.wordpress.com/related-articles/recovery-from-abuse/healing-emotional-memories/real-or-imagined-the-brain-doesnt-know/

resentment, because your case is getting stronger inside of you and your thinking has now shifted from short-term memory to long-term memory. When you build a case in your mind, your biology begins to change and your long-term thinking is now allowing bitterness to make a home in your body. It is being reinforced to eventually bring death to you in the end!

Anger and wrath are some more pieces of this negative armor. The first three (unforgiveness, resentment and retaliation) represent things that are going on in your heart internally. However, when anger and wrath breaks out, it is exterior. Hatred then sets the stage for the physical elimination of a person, meaning that you are destroying yourself, ultimately.

Violence is the act of all these things. It could come in the forms of fighting, striking, cursing, throwing, screaming, verbal or sexual abuse. Self-violence could look like addiction, self-cutting, mutilation of self or a host of other destructive behaviors. The last armor piece is death and murder. This represents physical murder, murder with the tongue, or self-murder, meaning suicide.

These are all very mean spirited and very evil. They are why you do not want a root of bitterness taking place in your heart. Hebrews 12:15 again says, "Looking diligently lest any man fall short of the grace of God; lest any root of bitterness springing up trouble you, and thereby many be defiled."

I understand that when we have been deeply hurt by someone, it is hard to walk the road of forgiveness. Forgiveness does not mean that we condone what someone has done. We don't condone others abusing or hurting us. That is not the goal. The goal is to overcome! We overcome it by laying it down and allowing the Lord to bring change in the person and to be set free from being corroded by bitterness and all the negative armor pieces that go with it. I understand that often times, forgiving someone is hard.

However, the only thing harder than offering forgiveness is living with resentment. We have the choice to choose a life of forgiveness where we free ourselves and others, or a life of resentment where we live as prisoners for someone else's crime. Always choose freedom.

Choosing to Forgive

I want to take a moment to activate the power of forgiveness into your own life. I recommend that you set aside at lead ten minutes and go to a quiet place where you won't be disturbed. If needed, be willing to repeat this for a few days in a row, or more, if needed.

The Lord's Prayer:

"After this manner therefore pray you: Our Father which art in heaven, Hallowed be thy name. Thy Kingdom come, Thy will be done in earth, as it is in heaven. Give us this day our daily bread. And forgive us our sins, as we forgive those that sinned against us. And lead us not into temptation, but deliver us from evil: For thine is the kingdom, and the power, and the glory, forever. Amen." Mt 6:9-13 KJV

Instructions: Pray and ask God to reveal the names of people (whether living or dead), organizations, political parties, churches and denominations, and situations that you are holding unforgiveness towards. Include yourself and God if it applies.

Take a few minutes and allow God to speak to your heart and create the list below:

____

____

____

____

____

____

____

____

Now, looking at the list, take a moment to ask the Holy Spirit to bring His presence into the room. When you are ready, pray this prayer:

> *"Father God, I ask that you forgive me for every person: organization or political party: any church or denomination; or any situation that I have held unforgiveness towards. Father God, today as an act of my will and obedience to your Word, I choose to forgive and release every person, organization, or situation that has hurt or offended me. I release it to You. In the name of Jesus I pray. Amen."*

Now take your pen or marker and as an act of obedience to the Word of God...cross out the name and say to yourself, "I choose to forgive….."

Place your hand over your heart and pray this prayer:

"Father God, I thank you for healing me today of offenses, rejection, injustice, harshness, cruelty and pain that others have caused. Thank you for healing the hurt in my heart! In Jesus' name, Amen."

From this day forward, as God reveals to you anyone else you have not forgiven, by an act of your will and obedience to God's word: repeat the above process. Freedom will come!!

It has been our great pleasure to serve under pastor Ron Schoenherr and teach Pathways to Wholeness. I recommend you go online and take the curriculum. It will change your life.

rcministry.org/pathways-to-wholeness/
Pathways to Wholeness, seminar workbook: 2016 Restoration Christian Ministries

The Physiology of Thought

Your mind will always believe everything you tell it. Feed it hope. Feed it truth. Feed it love.

Let's begin by looking at the position and condition of our hearts. When we accept Jesus as our Lord and savior, our heart position immediately changes and all that Jesus is and ever will be is given to us. We are accepted and justified before the Lord as if we had never sinned. However, the condition of our hearts doesn't change immediately! That is a process that begins with our thoughts, which is a powerful place to start with because that not only motivates our decisions, but it is really where the enemy can get us if we are not careful.

Romans 8 confirms that our flesh is the carnal mind, however our goal is to have the mind of Christ! So, our heart condition will change when we learn to walk in the spirit and not in the flesh. We are born into sin and were trained to act and think in opposition to God's ways. When we begin the process of "working out our salvation," an aspect of that is that our mind would be conformed to God's ways of thinking and doing. That is the whole process of sanctification: to move from operating from the soul to the Spirit! This is confirmed in Ephesians 4:23 where it says, "We are to be renewed in the spirit of our mind."

There is a difference however, between the carnal mind and the mind of the spirit. Our carnal mind is not regenerated, so therefore it is against God and cannot be renewed. Only through the Spirit can our mind be regenerated and renewed, which is a repetitive process that occurs in the brain.

Your brain is always gathering information and is constantly giving off wavelengths. These wavelengths are divided into four types: alpha, beta, theta and delta.

The first type of wave is the alpha wave. The alpha wave is our conscious thinking in the sub-conscious mind. What does that mean? It just means that it is in a relaxation state where there is an expanded awareness of the world around us. It is the birthplace of creativity and deductive reasoning. Alpha waves occur about twice a day, typically when you wake up and when you go to sleep. You can also learn to slow down your processing for creativity if needed. If you have too little, you may become anxious. If you have too much, you'll do little more than daydream and may find yourself unable to focus. It could also be called optimal relaxation and is a great place to set goals and be creative. So the alpha waves are the connection between the spirit and the physical world of your body.

The beta wave length is our conscious wavelength. It fires off at 14-20 hertz per second and since it is a very quick firing, it is the source of conscious thought used in critical thinking, writing, and socialization. Beta also handles problem solving. We often drink coffee and tea to stimulate this. It is the first kind of brain waves and is largely responsible for connecting your soul to your body.

Theta waves are subconscious thinking. This is what connects your spirit and soul. It is where God talks to you and where you hear from the Lord. It's the intuition, meditation, emotional connection, and yet another source for creativity. It is a place that you can be sleepy and where you may feel very raw emotions. This brain wave is our connection to the Holy Ghost.

Finally, delta waves come when we are in a deep sleep and run at 0-4 hertz. Interestingly, It is most often found in highest measure in infants and small children. It is very much a healing and restful sleep state that brings restoration to your body. It is why you are tired when you are sick and why we need to get enough sleep at night for our bodies to function well.

So the alpha, beta, and theta waves are how you process and think. They are necessary for facilitating images, creative thinking and creating personality. Transformation requires change and that change in the soul occurs through a process called neural-plasticity. This is how all of your behaviors can change your brain for the positive or the negative and is going to be the key to renewing your mind!

There are three keys to help assist in this change. When you have a thought, or are training to do something new, you have numerous chemicals that flood your brain to create short-term memory. They increase the amount of firing as you practice them. For example, if I'm learning piano, when I begin chemicals fire off and induce structural changes in my short-term memory. This cascade improves with each practice. But when you first get started, you don't have enough change to support that in long-term memory. So that's why you have to practice again and again. After a while, it does begin to alter the structure and memory. That changes the connections, which begin to change and go from short-term to long-term memory. Getting short-term to convert to long-term requires repetition.

So how does this apply in the context of a life? I'll use myself as an example. I did not accept Jesus as my savior until I was 24. Everything I had learned up to that point was carnal. All that I learned was derived from my generational heritage and life experience and because of this, my life from age 0-8 was largely a train wreck! So consider this, a thought that occurs over and over again actually becomes permanently apart of your biology. What I had learned as I grew to maturity was now resident within and a part of my biology. How did that change?

Our great God's heart is to rewrite His laws on our heart and spirit. He desires to train us so that His law is not just in our spirit, but his law is a part of our personality as a human being. However, the enemy wants to train you as well and he tries to use the same pathway! He wants to give you the law of sin as opposed to the law of God. There is a battle that is going on, according to scripture, and very clearly laid out in Romans 6-8. So when I accepted the Lord, I engaged this process of neural-plasticity with the spirit in mind!

As Christians, we still have the law of sin in our being. It doesn't mean that we are possessed by a devil, it just that the law of sin has been reinforced in your fallen nature as it had been in mine from early on. So everything you perceive externally is recorded in your long-term memory, which becomes part of your biology. This is neural-plasticity. It is what we have played over and over and over again in the negative realm is a part of our biology. Everything that we replay in the positive realm is also apart of our biology. However, we want to have the renewed mind! Indeed, God commands us to renew our mind!

"A More Excellent Way" author: Henry W. Wright copyright 2009 Be in Health

It is confirmed in so many ways in the Word. When we accepted Christ, these are the things that you received: you received all the fullness of the Godhead, because He dwells in you.

"For in Him (Jesus) dwells all the fullness of the Godhead. The same power that rose Jesus from the dead dwells in you." Colossians 2:9

"But if the Spirit of Him who raised Jesus from the dead dwells in you, He who raised Christ from the dead will also give life to your mortal bodies through His Spirit who dwells in you." Romans 8:11

"By which have been given to us exceedingly great and precious promises, that through these you may be partakers of the divine nature, having escaped the corruption that is in the world through lust." 2 Peter 1:4

Truly, we have been given God's nature and we get to decide if we want to pick it up and use it. The process of thought in the renewing of your mind is there so that everything that you perceive externally is recorded in your long-term memory, which is apart of your biology. So many Christians serve sin and don't even know it! God wants us to be renewed! Your goal should be to have your armor of God on all the time! Never take it off and use the word of God as your source of truth and strength. Through this, you get to lead every thought and not be led by every thought.

As we discussed in the restoration chapters, you can have up to 120 thoughts a minute, give or take. You will typically have between 60-120 while the beta waves are active. If, in a perfect day, you were up and be awake all day long, that would be about 60,000 thoughts per day. I say this to tell you that you need to overthrow the fortified city of thinking that's in your biology. It's not hard to do because you're destined and created to do it! Your neural-plasticity will work with you because it always wants to change!

In the Garden of Eden, when Adam and Eve made the mistake of eating from the tree of the knowledge of good and evil, the spiritual understanding came to them and boom! They understood good and evil and saw that they were naked. They instantly were ashamed of their nakedness. The Lord came to walk with them in the cool of the evening, so they hid themselves because of shame, guilt, and fear. The Lord came and said, "Adam, where are you?" Adam said "I heard your voice and was afraid because I was naked." And the Lord said, "Who told you that you were naked?"

Notice, the Lord didn't say "Adam, you have developed a psychosis, you are chemically imbalanced. Where did you get that negative emotion?" The Lord never indicated that the source of Adam and Eve's thoughts were their own. The Lord said, "Who told you that?"

You are not the problem! The problem is how you are processing thought and where those thoughts come from! You have been trained the same way that Adam and Eve were trained. The question, "Who told you?" is powerful because it sets us free from shame! You have been trained in your families for almost 6,000 years to think in opposition to God. You have been taught to relate to one another in an improper way through anger, rejection, and bitterness.

Adam and Eve's thoughts were not their own. God wants us to remove those things that aren't of Him, which includes our thoughts. A good way to know if you are hearing from the Lord is recognizing if you have the fruits of the Spirit evident in your life. If you are not hearing from God, but from the enemy's camp, the fruits are going to be bitterness, rejection of self, God or others.

I can't reiterate enough that you aren't the problem! You were born into a fallen world! I love to use myself as an example because the Lord has helped walk me into complete freedom. I didn't get saved until I was 24. Because of this, I had 24 years of baggage that I was carrying. 24 years worth of hurt, anger, and skewed perceptions of the world, God, and myself. I had to begin the journey of renewing my mind and reshaping how I saw the world around me. I grew up believing many lies and I had to allow myself to become aware of the thoughts coming in and out my brain so that I could take them captive. This process does take time, but with endurance and your eye on the prize, it becomes second nature.

I encourage you to ask yourself, "Where am I going to end up with my thinking?" Do your thoughts lead you closer to God and to a place of life and freedom or do they lead you astray to a place of hopelessness and defeat? You have to hold every thought captive. Forgive yourself for the person you used to be and take responsibility for what is in the present. This will allow Him to lead you into future.

Remember, renewing your mind is not a one and done process.

It takes time. You will have to take it day by day and seed by seed...

The Limbic System-GAS

Another facet of our soul is the limbic system, which is a part of the brain and thus has tremendous impact on our soul. The Limbic system borders the cerebral cortex and the diencephalon. It constitutes many different processes but most frequently is linked to emotion.

Structurally, we have the amygdala, which is almond-shaped and is directly connected to fearful and anxious emotions. With the amygdala we have the hippocampus, which is primarily associated with memory, although there are other emotions involved. In addition there is the mammillary body, which is associated with memory and the connection between the amygdala and the hippocampus. Then there is the hypothalamus, which controls hormones via the anterior pituitary gland. It can exert widespread influence over our body's states to maintain homeostasis.

It also controls the two "H"'s which are big players in our body: Homeostasis and Hormones. The hypothalamus' primary role is to maintain a balance within all the systems all the time. It puts exertion on the autonomic nervous system and releases hormones primarily through the pituitary gland. The pituitary gland has an anterior portion and a posterior. The anterior pituitary releases six hormones. The posterior, all through signaling from the hypothalamus, releases two hormones. The anterior pituitary releases growth hormones, and a series of others including the follicle stimulating hormone, luteinizing hormone, adrenocorticotropic hormone, thyroid stimulating hormone and prolactin. Each of these hormones has a function unique unto itself. The growth hormone is that stimulates growth, cell reproduction, and cell regeneration. Follicle stimulating hormone is for development and reproduction. Luteinizing hormone is for testosterone and reproduction. Adrenocorticotropic hormone is for stress and our fear responses. Thyroid stimulating hormone regulates metabolism. Prolactin produces milk in females. They are all controlled via the hypothalamus.

The posterior pituitary releases oxytocin, and vasopressin. Oxytocin is known for social bonding and compassion. Vasopressin regulates blood pressure and urinary output.

So, why are these important to us? The limbic system connects your psyche and thoughts to your physiology. It is the mind-body connection. For all intents and purposes, it links the emotional side of your being to the physical side of your body and since the hypothalamus always wants to bring homeostasis, when you are overly stressed or taxed, there are two plays that occur. There are negative emotions and positive emotions. Either one, the system constantly needs to be in balance. The hypothalamus is in charge of keeping that balance so that it sends information and impulses to the body to slow it down or speed it up.

The connection between our soul, mind, will, emotions and body comes through the interplay and operation of these hormones within our body's systems. Consider that with our review of brain waves, short term and long-term memory, and neural plasticity and how memory becomes a part of your biology. These two systems of operation within our bodies are primary pathways by which our bodies synch with our souls.

Indeed, every emotion you have is connected to and within your body. And there is a process by which the Lord made our physiology to function because God loves order. Your thoughts have an order on how they process information that is very succinct and direct. We were never designed to live in a stressful state and to have all of our emotions constantly cascading and negatively affecting our body. As we go through life, we develop mechanisms to adapt and receive those stressors.

Thankfully, the Lord Jesus gave us peace. John 14:27 says, "Peace I leave with you, my peace I give unto you: not as the world gives, give I unto you. Let not your heart be troubled, neither let it be afraid."

He gave us peace because that is who He is. We read in Jeremiah 6:13-14, "For from the least of them even unto the greatest of them every one is given to covetousness; and from the prophet even unto the priest every one dealt falsely. They have healed also the *hurt of the daughter* of my people slightly, saying, Peace, peace; when *there is* no peace."

Sometimes in life we find ourselves moving at too high or fast of a pace. Culturally, everything is set for immediate gratification. So that pace of peace in times when there is no peace is Jesus calling you to put on His peace and His pace! It's a piece of our Holy armor and one of the fruits of the spirit. I developed a picture identifying what I am wrapped with. It is called Ever-Present. Jesus is given to us as a present. He is God's gift to us! When you receive a present, you get excited and can't wait to open it. When you open this box from Jesus, out of it comes the fruits of the spirit, which is love, joy, peace, patience, kindness, goodness, faithfulness, gentleness and self-control. All of that comes with this gift. Sometimes we get the gift and in our busy-ness we just ignore it and let it sit in the corner. We don't value the present and use the gifts because they're inside of us and we can take them for granted or default to old patterns or other ways of relating in life.

The truth is that all of the fullness of the Godhead resides in us. If it all resides in us, but we don't operate from and with the gifts He has given, it has no function or role or power in our lives to bring or maintain wellness. And worse, even if our life experiences have been positive, if the negative and being stored in your biology bombard them all, you will find yourself in sickness.

Fundamentally, it is an unloving and anti-Christ spirit. It comes most often when you are self-focused with a "me, myself, and I" attitude. These attitudes become patterns, which lead to addictions, fear and stress and we cannot forget or ignore the superglue that holds it all together, which is self-pity!

So it's important to ask yourself some questions daily and regularly:

/ What am I wrapped with?
/ What have I decided to be wrapped with in this moment?
/ Am I going to allow the presence of the flesh, the carnal body, to wrap me or am I going to pick up and empower yourself with the wholesome fruit of the spirit?

You will begin to see the power and dynamic of the positive and negative perspectives in our lives. The more mindful we are of those paths, the more strengthened and resolute we become in choosing well that leads to wellness!

We are reminded in II Timothy 1:7 "For God hath not given us the spirit of fear; but of power, and of love, and a sound mind." Imagine the reference to "power" here represents the Holy Spirit and perhaps the "love" represents our Father God. Perhaps the "sound mind" comes from Jesus, the word of God. He has given it all to us for our use and empowerment, but it is always our choice to use it.

Let's explore this a little further. Hans Sale developed the term "general adaptation syndrome", which refers to how you manage stress. There are 3 pieces to this. The first phase is the alarm phase, which refers to your "fight or flight" mechanism. Your alarm stage was designed to reset in order to cope with short-term changes in the environment. When this happens, it releases the hormones of cortisol and epinephrine.

Each of these has a function. The cortisol will decrease pain, inflammation and your immune response in the short-term. The epinephrine increases your heart rate, breathing, muscle strength and contraction, as well as releases sugar. It wants to use sugar as fuel for your muscles so you can run away from that proverbial "tiger in the jungle." It's safe to assume that many of us may not be living in the wilderness escaping wild beasts, but our body doesn't know the difference between stressors. So if you allow yourself to become overwhelmed by the stress of sitting in traffic or taking the kids to school, you are in your alarm phase and you've utilized the fuel and saved the day! The system is designed to need to reset. If it doesn't reset, it moves into what is called the resistance phase. Life circumstances, a broken heart, hurt relationships, financial stress, job stress or any number of other things cause that same release of cortisol and epinephrine. However in this case, this can occur for long periods of time under sustained stress. And when sustained, this is where you begin to affect your psychology and physiology and your body actually can cope for weeks, months, years and even decades with this cortisol - epinephrine push. The result is now a elevated heart rate, elevated blood pressure, muscle tension, abnormal blood sugar as well as a weakened immunes system. So whenever you have negative thoughts, you are triggering this mechanism and cascade of negativity, which robs your wellness.

With this level of stress and cascade, your brain is under duress. It then sends a signal to your gut, which kills off all your healthy bacteria which then takes wellness away from your physical body through your emotions and soul life.

Whenever we feel like we are in trouble, it is triggering the resistance stage to stay on. That is not what we were designed to do or how we were designed to live! The heartbeat goes up, but never comes down. It just stays high. All of us are different and some can handle this longer than others without an emergency.

Then we get to the exhaustion phase when we are unable to take it anymore. So your high heart rate will continue along in a straight line, but at some point that line will drop straight down when you just can't cope anymore. At that point your metabolic functions are no longer able to keep pace with your long-term stress and your body becomes diseased.

Truly, each of us handles stress differently. A tombstone says R.I.P., which is a reference to "rest in peace." An alternative inscription could just as easily say S.K.M. for "stress killed me." Heart problems, strokes, as well as a number of other things develop from stressful situations. Jesus once said that a man's heart will fail him for fear, which is rooted in stress and anxiety. The direct and tangible benefit of taking up peace from the Prince of Peace is the opportunity to circumvent these issues. Christ didn't give us a spirit of fear, stress or anxiety, but of power, love and a sound mind! When we are filled with the fellowship of the Lord, the trinity, we are free from fear and have constant connection and courage from God.

It is imperative that we instruct our limbic system to whom it is to bow. There are two choices: it can bow to the kingdom of heaven or the enemy's kingdom. The kingdom of heaven is designed to bring you health, but the kingdom of darkness wants you to rob that from you and bring sickness so that you die early, thereby aborting the fulfillment of your God-given destiny.

We were designed to manage stress. Stress was not designed to manage us. So what or whom is managing you? Is it God's kingdom managing you or are the enemies "gifts" and tricks and deceptions managing you? What do you ultimately want to be wrapped with in your spirit, soul, and body? We do have consequences for every thought that we hold captive. It must become our goal and discipline to choose the fruits of the spirit and the kingdom of God. The kingdom of God is righteousness, peace and joy in the Holy Spirit.

Chapter 8

REBUILD YOUR SPIRIT

Sacred Rhythms

When I refer to sacred rhythms, I am referring to practices that we implement into our lives that help set a pace for our souls to rest in God. A rhythm is something that repeats itself. It's a repeated pattern. We need to create rhythms and discipline in our lives in order to create momentum and room for breakthrough. Use prayer for an example. The goal of prayer is to be able to connect us to God. It helps create relationship and history with him. If we pray for just a few minutes every few days or so, we aren't really making room for that relationship to grow. Just like if we only talk to one of our friends for a few minutes once a month, we aren't going to see that friendship grow. So, it's important to make time and room to pray daily and consistently. In this chapter, I want to go over some of the sacred rhythms that I have incorporated in my own life and that I encourage all my patients to incorporate as well. I believe that sacred rhythms are the key that opens the door to total health.

Prayer

Throughout Jesus' time here on earth, he was constantly going before God in prayer. He knew the importance prayer has in the life of a believer. In Romans 12 it says, "Rejoice in hope, be patient in tribulation and continuing steadfastly in prayer." Just as Jesus was, we need to be steadfast in prayer. It brings peace and the ability to cast your cares on Him. When you are quiet enough, you can hear back from Him.

Colossians 4:2 says, "Continue earnestly in prayer. Be vigilant in it with thanksgiving." Prayer and thanksgiving go hand in hand. When we are vigilant and earnestly praying, we have thanksgiving because prayer is faith in action. You are asking for things that you don't yet see. Sometimes God answers prayer in a minute and others take longer. I have had times where I will wait before God and right at the very last moment, when it is all going to go down…boom! God will show up and He answers our prayer! Jokes are often made that he comes at the 59th minute of the 11th hour but truth is He always comes through! He is just so good all the time.

Some patients have asked me, "Where do our prayers go? Why pray if God will work all things together for our good?" In Revelation 5:8 it says "And when he had taken the book, the four beasts and four and twenty elders fell down before the Lamb, having every one of them harps, and golden vials full of odors, which are the prayers of saints." It is glorious because He takes all of our prayers and brings them before the Lamb of God where they become beautiful incense to the Lord. We are all his saints and our prayers are brought before Him as incense. How fabulous is that?

I grew up in a family that never encouraged or built me up. As a result, I never thought I was great at anything or could ever amount to anything. I was often told how ugly I was and how I needed to get my cellulite under control because guys don't like cellulite. I was a tomboy and there was nothing feminine about me. Bear in mind that I grew up with 5 brothers and am still a bit of a tomboy who knows how to hold a gun!

What that said, it left a mark on me and I learned to believe that I was not beautiful. It was sad and it broke me. I even used to struggle with deciding what to wear every day! It was just ridiculous! It was when I began to disciple a dear friend of mine that I got a break through over this battle. She was dating a guy who was going through a divorce. Life was hard for her. During this time, I had a particularly hard morning and was just so sick of the battle with clothing and my life. I pulled into an airport parking lot and cried out, "Lord, I am not moving from this spot until you talk to me and start giving me some hope about doing something! I can't live without self-esteem, and I can't live without a purpose and I can't live being in so much pain!" The Lord so kindly responded to me with Isaiah 60. It reads "The sun shall no more, be your light by day. Nor for brightness shall the moon give light to you. But the Lord shall be to you an everlasting light. He will be your God. He will be your glory and He will be your Beauty." I immediately became undone because God was calling me "Beautiful." God met me in my prayer and gave me a revelation that forever changed my life.

Because of that prayer, I realized that my beauty didn't need to come from the outward appearance. I was free to allow my beauty come from the inside. So, I would begin to pray each day asking God what I should wear! It may seem trivial to some, but God cares about the little things just as much as He cares about the big things. He cares about it all! If you would just go to Him in prayer, He will be that expression that you need and meet you there.

Fasting

Fasting is perhaps the least pursued and most resisted of all sacred rhythms! Years ago, I felt led by the Lord to go on a worship fast. So I would worship for an hour per day to one CD specifically. I did this for 40 days. It took me to a whole new place in God. Have you ever fasted with just worship? An hour of pure worship and dedication to God could be the key to your breakthrough. It brings breakthrough into your life and draws you closer by the renewing of your mind.

Consider this: Health is maintained through rest. Instantly we think of sleep when we think of rest. While sleep is the body's way of getting rest, our spirit needs rest as well. The way our spirit gains rest and strength is by fasting. It is the act of putting our flesh "down" through depriving it from its customary forms of satisfaction that our spirit gains supremacy and strength. Nobody really likes to talk about this one, because nobody likes to fast, especially from food! For me, it is easier for me to fast two meals a day and eat one. When I feel hungry throughout the day, I remind myself that I am doing this because I love the Lord and He is going to reveal Himself to me.

Scripturally, there is much precedence for this practice. In Isaiah 58 we read, "Yet they seek me daily, and delight to know my ways, as a nation that did righteousness, and forsook not the ordinance of their God…Why have we fasted, they say, and you see not? Why have we afflicted our soul and you take no knowledge? Behold, in the day of your fast you find pleasure and exploit all your laborers." The fast here reveals the inconsistency of their lives that needs to be redressed.

Ezra 8: 21 says, "Then I proclaimed a fast there, at the river of Ahava, that we might humble ourselves before our God, to seek of him a right way for us, and for our little ones, and for all our possessions." The purpose of this fast was that they were seeking direction. This is a common and in fact, often, a baseline for why people fast: to discover the right way or direction at a juncture or crossroads in life.

Nehemiah 1 says, "Now on the 24th day of this month, the children of Israel were assembled with fasting and sackcloth and dust on their heads." The people were repenting and confessed their sins in this instance of fasting. For us, fasting can bring on repentance when we have strayed and can become an opportunity for confession. Confession as we know brings healing.

Psalm 35:13 says, "But as for me, when they were sick, my clothing was sackcloth: I humbled my soul with fasting; and my prayer returned into my own bosom." Here we find that fasting brings humility and a restoration of and vitality to prayer life.

Hunger is such a great persuader! It is like having that inner sounding in your heart that reminds you that you are fasting because you need to hear from God. The whole point is to get low and to draw upon the presence of the Lord. There is such power in coming before the Lord and acknowledging that you need Him. When Esther had to go before the king, she told Mordecai to gather the people and to pray and fast for three days before she went so that the Lord would prepare the king's heart so that he might extend his scepter towards her. Otherwise, to approach the king without invitation could get you killed. So she gathered her people to pray and to come in agreement to bring heaven to earth so the circumstances can change. Those prayers were effective because the King extended his scepter to her despite her cultural trespass.

Jesus gave the greatest example of fasting when he was led and tempted by Satan in the wilderness. In Luke 4 it says, "And Jesus being full of the Holy Spirit returned from the Jordan, and was led by the Spirit into the wilderness. Being forty days tempted of the devil and in those days he did eat nothing: and when they were ended, he afterward hungered." Isn't it amazing what He did for us? His example is all we need in life. In those 40 days, he ate nothing! Hungy? I would think so! The point is that Jesus is our example and if He fasted (for 40 days!), we should follow in His ways.

From that fast He gained strength and the approval of His father. He took territory in the spirit for you and me to fast and to deflect Satan off of our lives so that he can't have any authority over us. Fasting is an honor, but not easy. So you need to be in prayer to see what and when the Lord leads. It is a powerful sacred rhythm.

Spiritual Hunger

As I mentioned earlier, physical hunger is the greatest persuader that we know of, amen? When you are hungry, you are hungry. It will move you. It motivates you to go after what you want and that is food. Just as our bodies hunger, so do our spirits. Our spirits have a natural hunger for God. You were designed to desire God and once you taste his goodness, you crave more.

Psalm 34:10 says, "The young lions do lack, and suffer hunger: but they that seek the LORD shall not lack any good thing." When we seek the Lord's face, we are not going to lack or suffer hunger, unless it is a spiritual hunger, which pulls us back in to Him. In Matthew 5 we find that "blessed are those who hunger and thirst for righteousness, for they shall be filled." His greatest desire is for us to seek Him so that He can fill us with his promises. He wants to see us overflowing so that we become a river of living water flowing to others.

In Matthew 6:33 it says, "But seek you first the kingdom of God, and his righteousness; and all these things shall be added unto you."

It is in the seeking after Him that your spirit man goes up higher and wants to have an ever-ascending climb unto the Lord and the things of the Lord. He doesn't hide Himself from us. He's right there; ready to be found when we seek him.

When my boys were young, we would play hide and go seek. I would never hide so well that they couldn't find me. I always hid in such a way that they could find me easily. Likewise, the Lord's heart is so full of love towards us, just as mine is for my boys. He makes himself easy to find. It is the easiest game of hide and seek there is, but you must keep asking, seeking, and knocking.

Journaling

"Your life is your story. Write well. Edit Often." Susan Stattan

Let's look at another seed we can plant to grow wellness in our lives Journaling. How does journaling rise to the level of being part of our spiritual rhythm? Scripture has so much to say about the importance of writing things down! Thus, an exploration of the value and purpose of journaling is worthwhile.

Journaling can carry the power of a decree in our lives. In Nehemiah 9:38 it says, "And because of all this we make a sure covenant, and write it; and our leaders, Levites, and priests, seal it." It becomes like a law and a decree when we write things down. That is a great reason to write things down because decrees release power to cause things to happen!

In Esther 8:8 it was commanded, "Write you also for the Jews, as it pleases you, in the king's name, and seal it with the king's ring: for the writing which is written in the king's name, and sealed with the king's ring, may no man reverse." There is something about writing

something down that solidifies it and makes it irrevocable. There is a permanency about writing that is significant and notable.

It's power gets even more poignant! It says in Psalm 87:6, "The LORD shall count, when he registers the people, that this man was born there. Selah." So, He cares enough to have an account of who you are and where you are. Our names are written in the Book of Life. We also know that He inscribes us on the palm of His hand. If the Lord values our name so much that He has us written in His book and His palm, then our writing carries weight and value in our own lives.

The fruit of the spirit is another thing we are to document in our lives. We are told to write them on the tablet of our heart. That takes journaling to another level. Writing on paper puts a physical expression and externalization to what is within, but when we "write on the tablet of our heart" that requires intention at another level in the Spirit.

Hebrews 10:16 says, "The Holy Spirit also is a witness to us: for after this he had said before, This is the covenant that I will make with them after those days, says the Lord, I will put my laws into their hearts, and in their minds will I write them." He is all about writing things onto your heart!

We also write things down to leave a legacy. 2 Peter 3:1 says, "This second epistle, beloved, I now write unto you; in both of which I stir up your pure minds by way of remembrance." Writing gives you a place to remember God's faithfulness and impart to future generations.

Since we are exploring the act of journaling, let's go over some other health benefits it carries:

It brings clarity.
It is an opportunity to clear your mind for higher thinking. When writing or journaling, I often ask God to unlock what I need to see in what I wrote, after I write it. I will write about an emotion I am having and I will ask the Lord to show me what it is that He wants to reveal to me. I then go on to document what I hear Him saying.

It helps you process.
Many times we can get caught up in our own life circumstances and emotions, that it can be hard to process what it actually going on inside of our heart. I have found that journaling helps strengthen my ability to be soothed and comforted by the Lord. It allows me to release any negative emotions that I am carrying and bring them before the Lord.

It provides records of my past.
It allows me to recount my life experiences and gives me insight into my thought processes. It helps document the journey that I have taken to get me to where I am today. It allows me to have gratitude because it shows me how I've progressed. It shows that I am going from glory to glory and enhances my own self-trust, which is a powerful weapon when the accuser brings lies to mind.

It releases the past.
I have been known to write things down that were considered "dirty" or painful from my past. I would then burn them as a sign of releasing my past. There is significance in releasing experiences and people from the past, because it takes your power back. You don't have to carry the pain those people or experiences caused anymore and it brings freedom. Freedom, as we know, boosts your immune system! Emotional freedom is immunity for your body.

You feel accomplished.
It increases your possibilities because it allows you to keep track of your dreams and the territory or spiritual ground you have taken in Christ. It helps you to think bigger as you start aiming higher in life! As we process our emotions with the Lord, it helps reduce self-limiting beliefs and you get even more break-through. Before you know it, you've taken ground and you can think bigger about your destiny and where you are headed.

Writing increases commitment.
It becomes visual and as you take increased ground in journaling, day in and day out, you become more committed to it as you see and experience the good fruit that seed yields.

confinedtosuccess.com/benefits-of-journaling-for-mental-health/

Journaling does more for us than just help us spiritually or emotionally. It also helps us physically! Let's talk about the physiology of journaling. When you write, your brain is activated. When you put pen to paper, you stimulate a group of cells called the reticular activating system. It filters to process information to the forefront of your mind. It allows you to focus and triggers your brain to pay close attention. It is a calming and meditative tool, as well as a stress coping mechanism. Remember, reducing stress means reducing cortisol and you thereby increase your immune function.

We went over the story of Amalek in the declarations section, but it also applies to this section as well. The Lord encouraged Moses to write the details of the victory against the Amalekites and to rehearse it in the hearing of Joshua. God promised he would utterly wipe out the record of the Amalekites. Moses had to write it down for a memorial in a book, so that it could be rehearsed among the people. Moses owned it by experience and Joshua recited it so that he too owned it and so that it could be spoken of and repeated again and again.

That is the power of the recorded testimony! What we have written becomes testimony that empowers you and others when spoken out. Freedom then comes to the people in the remembrance of the victory that God has in Christ for each of us individually.

Writing and journaling are often overlooked tools in our arsenal to spiritual and mental health and strength. Yet it is a powerful mechanism to offload, process feelings, and express the breadth of our life experiences, which allows for growth. Your life is your story. Write well. Edit often.

Cheer Myself Up In The Lord

"Remember the joy of the Lord is your strength" NEH *8:10*

A favorite and easy to cultivate seed in life that brings rich reward is laughter! Laughter is yet another key aspect to our wellness and

wholeness and it's also Biblical! I love to seek laughter because we need to laugh more than we do. Statistics show that the average adult laughs or smiles just 17 times a day while the average child is at least double that! I can't encourage you enough to laugh more!

We read in Psalm 126:2, "Then was our mouth filled with laughter, and our tongue with singing: then said they among the nations, The LORD has done great things for them." Job 5:22 also says, "At destruction and famine you shall laugh: neither shall you be afraid of the beasts of the earth."

God's solution for challenges and difficulty is laughter. We are to laugh right in the face of our enemy when times are tough. It is not only imperative, but powerful that you laugh! It accomplishes more than you know. It breaks the heaviness of the battle. To put into perspective, when has God actually not shown up and shown off when you cast your cares on Him? That is cause for laughter! We know what the outcome will be!

Proverbs offers great instruction and wisdom in this mater. Proverbs 15:13 says, "A merry heart makes a cheerful countenance: but by sorrow of the heart the spirit is broken." Proverbs 17:22 says "A merry heart does good like a medicine: but a broken spirit dries the bones." Interestingly enough, your bones house your immune system. So when your spirit is broken, you begin to attack your own immune system. When you're laughing, and when you have joy unspeakable, your immune system is strengthened and correspondingly you lower the chance of heart attacks and other forms of sickness.

Another benefit it laughter is that it increases your oxytocin levels, which decreases cortisol, the stress hormone. It is also heralded as a painkiller as well as helps in lowering blood pressure.

I had a patient who was in his sixties, who was actually a chiropractor. He had a disease called ankylosing spondylitis. What that means is that the vertebra would fuse one on top of the other, until you become stiff all the way up your spine. Unfortunately, the cause of this is unknown. You just begin to build connective tissue over the top of each vertebra, which hardens each joint. It has a candlewax, flowing appearance all the way across the spine. This gentleman decided that he did not want this condition to steal his joy, so he set out to laugh! While medically, ankylosing spondylitis is un-healable, God healed him through laughter!

So laugh! Be joyful and celebrate! Laugh at the enemy! I know that this is difficult to do in the midst of pain, but as you try and purpose in your heart to do that, you will be successful. You can build your own immune system back to strength.

Section 3

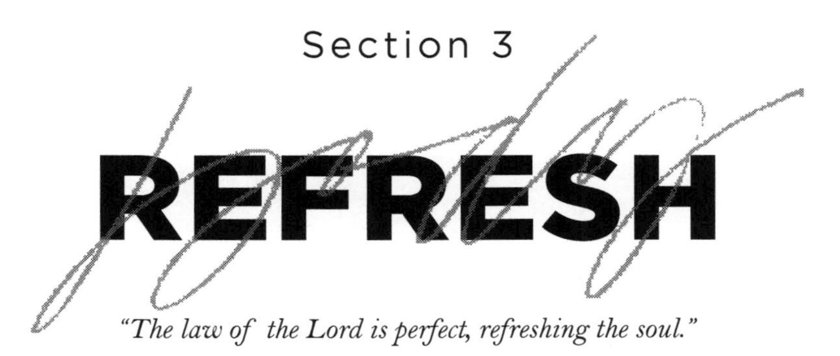

REFRESH

"The law of the Lord is perfect, refreshing the soul."

Psalm 19:7 NIV

//

We have now walked through what it looks like to rebuild our foundations as well as how to bring restoration to it. The beauty of our journeys to complete wellness is that it is never-ending. The Lord is faithful to continue to reveal his perfect will for our health as we continue through life. In different seasons of my own life, The Lord has come to bring refreshment to my body, soul, and spirit. Let's explore together what that refreshment might look like.

Chapter 9

REFRESH YOUR BODY

I. Antioxidants

I want to introduce you to the power of anti-oxidants. Let's begin by understanding what a free radical is. A free radical is a cellular killer that wreaks havoc by damaging DNA, altering biochemical compounds, corroding cell membranes, and destroying cells outright. In a very real sense, the free radical process in our bodies is similar to the process that causes an apple to turn brown if you slice it open and expose it to air. It is as though our bodies rust from the inside out. When the process gets worse, it can cause tumors, hardening of the arteries, macular degeneration, and not to mention wrinkled skin, to name just a few.

Your body is constantly replacing and repairing free-radical damaged cells. However, the way we live and abuse our bodies and ourselves, we are bombarded with more free radicals than they can handle. By supplementing with antioxidants, we help our bodies keep up with the carnage and can even get ahead of the game and reverse the damage.

So, what are antioxidants? Antioxidants are compounds that render free radicals harmless and stop the chain reaction formation of new free radicals. They have numerous health benefits including:

/ Repairing damaged molecules.

/ Blocking metal radical production. Some antioxidants have a chelating effect and they can grab toxic metals like mercury and arsenic, which can cause free radical formation, and "hug" them so strongly to prevent any chemical reaction from taking place.

/ Stimulating gene expression and endogenous antioxidant production. Some antioxidants can stimulate your body's genes and increase your natural defenses.

/ Promotes cancer cells to "commit suicide." Some antioxidants can provide anti-cancer chemicals that halt cancer growth and force some cancer cells to self-destruct (apoptosis).

In his book *The Antioxidants*, Richard A. Passwater, PhD, says that humans have one of the longest natural lifespans in the animal kingdom, most likely because of the wealth of antioxidants in our omnivorous diet. Human bodies also produce antioxidant enzymes that cannot be found in other creatures.

"Our natural antioxidant processes compensate for one another, covering up momentary deficiencies by their overlap," Dr. Passwater says. Many people think that taking just a few antioxidants is sufficient to maintain optimal health, but I strongly disagree. Instead, you must get a *wide variety* of antioxidants daily to maintain your wellbeing.

Antioxidants can be divided into three major groups:

- / Carotenoids: These have yellow, orange and red pigments synthesized by plants like tomatoes and carrots.
- / Allyl Sulfide: found in garlic and onions.
- / Polyphenols (also known as phenolics) which give fruits, berries and vegetables their vibrant color.

Anti-oxidants are often times the secret weapon when it comes to achieving and maintaining health and wellness! So, load up on your daily dose of berries!

jonbarron.org/article/antioxidants-part-1

II. Hormones

Hormones play a crucial part is how of bodies operate on a daily basis. Everything from our appetite, mood, critical thinking abilities, and waist-line is affected by our hormones. Over the years, I've learned that in order to accurately address our hormones, we must first address our diet. I could write an entire book on hormones (there are many great ones out there) but to sum up my findings, here is what I suggest:

1. Add cultures and fermented foods to your diet because they promote healthy digestion and helps balance hormone levels.
2. Try your best to eliminate grains, sugar and fructose because they decrease seven of the 12 most important hormones in the body.

3. Avoid or limit alcohol. Alcohol decreases your human growth hormone (HGH), one of your most potent built-in anti-aging hormones. Having just one alcoholic drink per day can decrease your HGH by 75%!
4. Add a magnesium supplement to improve your sex hormone levels.
5. Add high-quality protein from meat and fish, as well as healthy fats such as egg yolk, lard, and grass-fed butter. This will improve progesterone and DHEA secretion.
6. Add supplements to help increase progesterone levels including vitamin A. As a general rule, fat-soluble vitamins will have a beneficial effect on sex hormones.

Cortisol and Adrenaline

When it comes to resetting your body's hormone levels, two powerful hormones play a vital role. Cortisol and adrenaline. These are the two main stress hormones. Adrenaline is associated with acute (fight-or-flight) stress, whereas cortisol is long lasting and high levels can chronically affect you. Over time, high stress hormones make your body store fat, especially in your belly. High cortisol is also linked to depression, food addiction, and craving high-sugar foods. In other words, stress can make you fat.

I believe that weight loss is a result of a calm mind and body, particularly for women. To maintain physical and mental calmness, stay away from caffeine, sugar, and processed foods, and develop a contemplative practice. For me, that's the word of God. I love doing word studies of each individual fruit of the spirit (love, joy, peace, patience, kindness, goodness, faithfulness, gentleness, and self-control). I ask the Holy Spirit how I can pull from these words each and every day. I have found that this helps decrease my cortisol levels, because I am bringing into alignment the word of God over my body and my mind.

Leptin and Ghrelin

Two other important hormones are leptin and ghrelin. Leptin is nature's appetite suppressant. When you've had enough to eat, leptin signals your brain to stop eating. However, if you have too much stored fat, your fat cells produce excess leptin, causing leptin's normal function to shut down because it's been overwhelmed. It therefore never signals your body to say, "I'm full." So the more fat you carry, the more likely you'll be in an endless cycle of never feeling full. Ghrelin, dubbed the "hunger hormone," is leptin's opposite. The more ghrelin you have in your system, the hungrier you are. Ghrelin works by activating the brain's reward response to highly addictive sweet and fatty foods which makes you crave them incessantly.

To reset ghrelin and leptin, the solution is simple: get more sleep! New research has shown that even low levels of sleep deprivation increase your ghrelin levels and lead to more body fat storage. For robust leptin function, reduce the amount of sugar in your diet to fewer than twenty grams per day and eat zinc-rich foods such as seeds, chicken, oysters, and cashews to balance out leptin. Just as important, slow down your eating. By slowing your food intake, you give leptin more time to signal to your brain that you're full while also lowering your stress levels. More bang for every bite!

Estrogen

Too much estrogen in the body is associated with a higher body mass index (BMI). To reset estrogen, I recommend eating a pound of vegetables every day. The reason being is because the fiber from the vegetables eliminates excess estrogen, freeing you up for natural weight loss. Women should aim for forty-five to fifty grams of fiber *per day.* Be sure to increase your veggie intake slowly in order to avoid bloating and gas. Amen!

Testosterone.

Ladies, testosterone is not just for the guys. While women need less testosterone than men, we still need to maintain an optimal level for a healthy metabolism. If your testosterone is too low your muscles become flaccid or even doughy looking. Weak muscles means a slower metabolism! To reset testosterone, increase resistance training. Aim for a minimum of thirty minutes a day, three times a week. You don't have to specifically work out with barbells. Any weight-bearing exercise will do! Choose what you like and stick with it. For example, dance training can increase testosterone significantly and lower cortisol. In addition, cut back on sugar, maintain vitamin D levels, and supplement with branch amino acids.

The Hormone Cure, Sara Gottfried, MD, Scribner 2013
http://www.saragottfriedmd.com/why-cant-i-lose-weight-and-keep-it-off-hint-its-not-your-fault

III. Managing Stress

RESTing and how to do it!!

Rest is so important. We live in a culture where we pride ourselves on how busy we are, which is a sad game to play! There should be no shame when it comes to taking the time to rest and refresh our bodies!

Resting doesn't have to look like sleeping (although it is an ideal form)! Resting could look like a number of things. Any activity that helps you decompress and disconnect from the stressors in life brings healing to the body.

Here are a few ways you can integrate rest into your life.

Deep Breathes

Breathing is nature's natural de-stressor. Slow, deep breaths can help lower blood pressure and heart rate. I recommend starting and ending each day with three-six deep breathes. This can be done in the comfort of your own bed and will help bring refreshment to your body!

Progressive Relaxation

Many people struggle with feelings of overwhelming anxiety. This is when I will point them in the direction of progressive relaxation. Just squeeze, release, and repeat. Progressive relaxation involves tensing the muscles in one body part at a time to achieve a state of calm. The method is also a great way to help fall asleep.

Massage

Massage is one of the most healing techniques one can offer their body. Since we know that stress gets stored in our muscles, we are not only helping bring relief to our bodies but also our spirits and souls when we receive a massage.

Be Alone

This can be especially hard for those who have the blessing of a family! Most mama's can hardly even go to the bathroom alone! However, if you can take even just five minutes to escape and breathe, your mind, body and spirit will thank you.

Go Outside

Natural in itself has calming properties. If you're feeling stressed, take a brisk walk and notice how the wind blows through the trees. Watch as the leaves sway back and forth and take in the sound of them rustling.

Laugh

There is a reason that the Bible says that the joy of the Lord is our strength! Joy brings healing! Laughter's one of the sillier ways to beat stress, but there's science behind it A fit of laughter can increase blood flow and boost immunity.

Sunlight

I cannot tell you how much I love the sunshine. Our hearts cry out for the light in more ways than one! Over the years, we have become a society that rarely, if ever, gets out in the sunshine! Our time outside is only spent while walking from our homes to our cars and from our cars into our jobs. As a result, we are missing out on some key health benefits that the sun has to offer!

/ Lowers blood pressure: Sunlight helps release a compound called nitric oxide which is shown to help lower blood pressure.

/ Improves bone health. Vitamin D actually helps stimulate the absorption of calcium and phosphorous in the body.

/ Improves brain function: Sunlight has been shown to help promote nerve cell growth in the hippocampus, which is the part of the brain that is responsible for forming, organizing, and saving memories.

/ Alleviates depression: When exposed to sunlight, our brains actually produce more serotonin, which is the mood-enhancing chemical that helps fight of depression and sadness.

/ Improves Sleep Cycles: When in direct sunlight, our pineal gland produces melatonin, which is a natural sleep hormone.

/ Helps reduce symptoms of Alzheimer's: A study was done by the Journal of the American Medical Association that found that patients with Alzheimer's disease had fewer symptoms of depression, insomnia, and anger when exposed to bright light.

/ Helps strengthen the immune system: Vitamin D has been shown to fight against infection and disease.

Chapter 10

REFRESH YOUR SOUL

Armor

Let me propose a question to you: What if every thought you had did affect your body? What would it look like if you walked around in bitterness? As we discussed, bitterness has seven underlings that want to mold you. They are unforgiveness, retaliation, anger, wrath, hatred, violence, and murder, with your mouth or a gun, or in your thought life. What if every one of those thoughts that you had cascaded into your body and caused sickness and disease somewhere? What would that look like? It would look like sickness and disease.

Every time we go through an experience that has any sort of trauma attached to it, it affects us. It could have been as simple as being in a minor car accident or falling down the stairs. You could have been abused or had surgery. All of those thoughts have a physiological cascade in your body.

In God's word, it says that He wants you to be sanctified as Jesus Christ was sanctified. That means that you can pick up the divine nature of God! In Hebrews 2:11 it says, "For both he that sanctifies and they who are sanctified are all of one: for which cause he is not ashamed to call them brethren." Jesus is calling *us* brethren and desires for us to be sanctified. He desires for us to be set apart and made holy so that our thinking becomes the kingdom of God's thinking. He wants our thoughts to be one with His thoughts. His heart is for us to become so tightly woven with Him that we can't help but be victorious.

As we become victorious in life, we begin to take territory in the spirit. Then are we able to extend pure love and restoration to others. Imagine if our thinking was constantly immersed in the fruit of the spirit. What would it look like if we consistently walked in love? What would THOSE physiological cascades of thought be in our body? Instead of having evil things like bitterness, hate, and unforgiveness making it's home in our body, we instead became homes for peace, love, joy, and patience.

I can tell you what those manifestations would create in ourselves. It would produce long life. Psalm 91 says, "I will satisfy you and let you behold my salvation."

In Ephesians 6, we are told to put on the whole armor of God. So, when we live in sanctification, we keep it on. There is no such thing as taking the armor of God off and on in the Kingdom. In the Kingdom, we live in our armor. We live always on guard and aware of the Spirit of God. It is only in this way of life that we are able to fully come alive in God.

Beloved and beautiful people, I tell you that as sure as I am sitting here that if you step into what we are discussing here and take the journey on the pathway to wholeness, then you will begin to overcome and be victorious. You WILL see breakthrough begin to take root in your heart. Little by little and seed by seed you will see God come rushing in. As sure as I am sitting here, you will get victory in your life, and as you gain ground in your life, your whole heart will be restored. The beauty in this is that once you are restored, you can help bring restoration to others. That is the gift that God has called you to.

The Lord desires to have a union with us. Think about that statement for a second. The God of the universe, the God who created the sun and the moon desires to have a relationship with you and me.

John 15:7 says, "If you live in Me, abide vitally united to Me." We are to be abiding vitally to the Lord. It is similar to vital signs. These are signs that help you know how your body is functioning and how you are doing. A doctor or a nurse can take these vital signs and it is a report that gives a brief reflection of how you're doing.

If you treat the Lord and the word of God like a vital sign, you'll have an abiding life that is very close to the Lord. When we come back to the abiding life, all we can do is stand and just be ready for anything that comes our way. We will be able to recognize the enemy when he comes and laugh at him. Ephesians 6: 10 says, "Be strong in the Lord, be empowered in your union with Him." Draw your strength from Him! That strength has boundless might.

God gives us the belt of truth. This will help us recognize and resist the lies of the enemy. The belt of truth is the truth of God, which becomes your guiding light in the abiding life.

He gives us the breast-plate of integrity. This is the moral rectitude and right standing with God and having shod your feet in preparation to face the enemy with firm footed stability. All of that readiness is produced by the good news of the gospel of peace. And so, as the passage goes, your feet are shod with the preparation of the gospel of peace, but it is because you are firm-footed and you have that abiding life. Therefore when something comes up you aren't thrown around, you can simply stand.

Next, above all, is the shield of faith. It's important to understand that the shield it refers to is one of great defense and great safety. I think of the movie *Gladiator* where there are great examples of powerful shield work. The men at one point would line up and lock shields so that they become a literal fortress. When placed on the ground, the shields are nearly the height of the man holding them. All the missiles of the enemy would come at us and be totally deflected by our armor. All of this again is because of the abiding life Jesus offers.

We then put on the helmet of salvation. This is the deliverance and freedom that we receive through Christ. I should point out that the helmet comes through our thinking. The helmet lays and rests on our head because God wants us to have protection over our minds.

Last, but not least, is the sword of the spirit that wields the word of God. It is to our benefit to have the word of God abiding inside of us. We are instructed to pray at all times, on every occasion, and in every season in the spirit with all manner of prayer and entreating. Praise the Lord.

In closing, keep alert and watch for the Lord with purpose and perseverance. Be on guard, but don't stop living in perfect peace.

Unplugging

We live in a day in age where we have information being thrown at us from every angle. Thanks to social media, we know everything from what our friends are doing, where they are eating, to their personal political or religious views. We are constantly being bombarded by opinions, judgments, and suggestions. It's easy to get caught up in the hype and emotional intensity of the people around us.

Unplugging from people and situations is a powerful tool to restore balance to the soul! There are a few ways we can tell when it is time for us to unplug for a bit. For a mama, when we start feeling things happening over our kids is that sign it is time to unplug. When we are at work and someone is irritating us to the point where we begin to lose our peace, it is time to unplug. It's so easy to begin to pick up the burdens and the atmosphere of others around us. If we don't "unplug" from their atmosphere, we get pulled into their spiritual junk and are unable to operate in the strength of our own.

Using the analogy of the *I love Lucy* show, there was an episode where she became a switchboard operator back in the day when we used telephones. We also had to have an operator that plugged into different circuits on the switchboard. She had to unplug from the master switch port and plug into a different port to connect the call. So try to picture that scene and unplug from the other person whose atmosphere or soul is burdening you and plug in or connect to heaven. Release the power of the Holy Spirit in love over the situation so that he can do what only He can do!

Another way to unplug from a difficult situation or emotional experience is to clap your hands, snap your fingers, or shout out! A physical act releases breakthrough into the atmosphere and breaks the soul tension and reconnects you with the Lord. When we disconnect from a troubled situation, we are able to gain perspective and peace. There are many benefits of unplugging from life circumstances and plugging into the Holy Ghost so that He empowers us and He is free to do what He does best. As you engage in this practice, you will find He meets you in new ways and ways that most precisely minister to you.

The Power of Releasing

Yet another powerful way to get freedom in our soul is through what I call "releasing." This term describes any practice designed to allow for the release of emotions, trauma, fear or other "residue" that inhibits your emotional life. An entire book could be written on the resources available in this arena. Suffice it to say that trauma releases are a powerful technique used to accomplish this. Bethel Church in Redding, CA has a Transformation Center which offers Sozos, which is a very thorough prayer ministry leading an individual through a series of inquiries which reveal where you need healing. While the lists are extensive as to the ministries available for release to occur, the Holy Spirit is even more faithful to direct you in that regard!

The Power of Self Discipline

Self-discipline cannot be discounted in the process of strengthening and healing the soul. There are three things I'd like to share with you about training your thinking to empower you in that process. First is the red ruler. Second is the incontinence timer, and third is the dove.

Earlier in this book, I shared briefly about my journey and how I had to overcome negative thinking and thought patters. A part of this journey was a red ruler. Yes, a ruler. I used red rulers and taped them to my mirrors. The purpose of the ruler was to use the numbers on it from 0 to 12 as a scale to assess where I was in my thinking on that scale. When my emotions were lower on the scale, I had much more self-control than when my emotions were higher on the scale. It helped me become more self-aware as well as helped me acknowledge where my self-control levels were and allowed me to begin retraining myself.

I learned to perform a heart check and ask myself what was going on inside of myself. What was making me upset? Was it a comment someone made or an event that happened? Did I have any emotional needs that weren't being met? Why was I reacting as opposed to responding? In the training process, I learned a lot about myself and my emotions and how to work through things that were giving me that "high-octane" response inside my heart. I learned to discern when I was high on the scale and when I had to the invitation of the Holy Spirit. Ever so slowly, I began to see new patterns formed. I was able to catch myself before I would become so emotional that I would lose self-control and do something that I regretted. I knew that when I got to an 8, 9 or 10 on that ruler that I was losing self-control. It took a lot of hard work, but after a year I began to see positive changes.

During my search for a strong consciousness of God, a number of years ago I was listening to Pastor Beni Johnson talking about how her friend, Carol Arnott trained herself to be mindful of God's presence with a timer. She would wear this timer and it would buzz at various increments throughout the day. Beni had implemented this for herself and had great results. Knowing that I wanted to badly to be more conscious of God, I invested in one myself. So I got online and I ordered myself a timer but I could only find one designed to retrain incontinence! (The funny part is I now I get all these emails all the time from incontinence companies)! When I received it, I set it to alert me every ten minutes. Throughout my busy, busy days, it brought God into my awareness and recalibrated me back to Him. I loved it because every time it would buzz quietly on my side I would worship God inside or outside. I wore that timer for months and months and find it was one of the greatest investments I ever made! I still have that timer and I still wear occasionally just to sharpen my consciousness of God.

The third tool I've used comes from reading Pastor Bill Johnson's book, *Hosting the Presence.* In his book, he tells the story of Jesus getting baptized. Matthew 3:16 says, "After his baptism, as Jesus came up out of the water, the heavens were opened and he saw the Spirit of God descending like a dove and settling on him." Pastor Bill goes on to share that the Holy Spirit rested on Jesus like a dove. Doves are known to be easily scattered creatures, so you take each and every step with the intention of the dove on your shoulder. I learned to think about taking every step and action with the dove of the Holy Spirit on my shoulder and acting in such a way as to not disturb the dove from it's resting place. I decided that I would go get myself a fake bird to keep around my house as a reminder. Because I love birds, I looked around in all my boxes for a dove but didn't find one, but found another which I decided would be my reminder "dove." So I took this bird with me everywhere I went! I would take it to the store, to work, and I would even set it out in front of me when I would be working with a patient. This bird would go with me to remind me to continually access the Holy Spirit and that he is with me everywhere I go!

The combination of these three things have really enhanced how I process my thought life and because of it, I have so much more of a consciousness of the Holy Spirit and God's presence. I have improved greatly over the years and I know I will never fully arrive until I get to be with Him in Heaven. However, I have learned to love and enjoy the process because my walk with him is a never-ending journey in which I bow my knee to the Lord. My prayer is that this creates a hunger in you with creative ways that you can chase after His presence so that you can have your thought life so in tune with heaven that you can touch heaven and change earth.

Chapter 11

REFRESH YOUR SPIRIT

Thanksgiving

Our pile of seeds to sow into our Spirit continues to grow as we add in other spiritual rhythms. The seed of thanks carries great weight and power when we sow it. It is so important to simply sit and think about what you're thankful for. Everyday, I allow myself to grow in thanks for what I have. I am so thankful for my family and my darling, darling husband. I am thankful for my three handsome and absolutely wonderful sons. I am thankful for their wives and children to come. I am thankful for the green grass in this desert city of Redding, CA that we live in. I am thankful for the wonderful and beautiful home I live in, the healthy food that is on my table, and the clothes that I get to choose and wear everyday. I am grateful for the ability to speak and to have my health. My kids may not believe this, but I am thankful for my dog. I have a love-hate relationship with my dog, because he slobbers everywhere but that is a different story!

So the Lord tells us in Psalm 100:4 that as we "enter His gates with thanksgiving and go into His courts with praise. Be thankful unto Him and bless His name." A humble heart posture is required to bless God for everything to acknowledge that He is the one who has done it all and given it all to us! It causes us to be bowed down to Him and He is lifted up because of his goodness, which is shown through all the things we have to be thankful for.

This discipline is very important to me because I used to be a huge complainer. I'd complain about everything from doing the dishes to folding laundry to making dinner. Finally, the Holy Spirit interrupted my patterns and redirected me by asking, "What is your problem? You can't live your life complaining and being miserable. So take time with me during that time."

At that time we had cassette players. So I'd strap on a real cool yellow sporty one and I'd start just folding my laundry and doing my dishes while listening to worship music or an audio Bible. It was good for me to change my whole heart posture towards the Lord in the little things and in the big things. It also made way for me to experience his presence more! We are told that we usher in his presence with thanksgiving! How great is that?

I have grown much in the area of thanksgiving. The older I get, the more I realize how much I have to be thankful for. Even when life wasn't perfect, there are things to be thankful for.

Psalm 107:22 says, "If you bring your praise as an offering and your praise as a sacrifice." Isn't that interesting that sometimes it is a sacrifice to be thankful. It is absolutely a sacrifice when you are walking through some terrible situation such as the loss of a loved one, a sickness or disease, or a divorce to offer sacrifice when there is so much pain. It demonstrates a different way of connecting to God when we express gratitude in the midst of trial. When we thank God and say "it is well with my soul" right in the midst of the battle, it redirects your attention back to God. It helps reset your perspective. There are days where you literally need to force yourself to offer that sacrifice of thanksgiving and declare the words of God with rejoicing. However, if you do then blessing follows. It changes your heart posture.

Praise

Another seed we can sow in our sacred rhythms is Praise. Psalm 28:7 says, "The Lord is my strength and shield. My heart trusted in Him and I am helped. Therefore, my heart greatly rejoices and with my song, I will praise Him."

Praise postures your heart to come to a place where you know He is worthy. We are to come into his gates with thanksgiving and his courts with praise. Praise is powerful! I love what happens when praise spills from our hearts towards God. It opens up and postures our hearts to sense His presence and drawing near to us. In Psalm 92:3 it says, "Melodies of praise fill the air, as every musical instrument join with every heart and overflows with worship." When the melodies of praise join our hearts with instruments and sound, our hearts are opened. When we are praising and worshipping God, we are literally transforming and adding short-term memory strength to our brain. In turn, it adds more joy! This also helps you become transformed by the renewing of your mind during praise and worship.

Psalm 34 says, "Join me everyone and let us praise the Lord together. Let's make His name famous! Let's make His name glorious to all." Praise causes you to want to burst forth and tell everyone about the Lord and how good He is. Even in pain, He is still so, so, good to us.

Worship

A seed of great importance and substance in our sacred rhythms is worship. Worship is so close to praise that sometimes they seem to be the same thing. However, they are slightly different. One of the things that differentiate them is that worship means, “to bow down.” In the Hebrew, “shachah” is the word used for worship. It means to prostrate oneself or to bow down before the Lord. It is, in the primitive sense of the word, to depress or prostrate before royalty with humility.

The Lord loves to meet us in worship. Often times, you can literally sense the tangible presence of the Lord. Those are the moments that for me are so glorious and awe-inspiring because I want to carry that everywhere I go.

Worship is an expression of adoration.

The importance of worship is referenced in John 4:23 where it says, “But the time is coming, and is already here, when true worshippers will worship the Father in spirit, from the heart and the inner self and in truth. For the Father seeks such people to be his worshippers.” The Lord is searching the world for worshippers! God is a spirit, the main source of life and yet invisible to mankind, and those who worship him must do so in spirit and in truth.

Worship is powerful because your heart gets so connected with God that there are not words eloquently enough to describe it. God is seeking those who will worship Him in spirit and in truth. He created us in His own image and every one of us has a God shaped hole in our heart that He longs to fill. When we worship, God gets to come and do just that.

Creativity and Dance

Yet another sacred rhythm to incorporate into our lifestyle is creativity and dance. More specifically, dancing before the Lord. 2 Samuel 6:14-15 recounts how King David had been trying to move the ark. A series of events occurred but eventually the ark arrived at the house. It says, "So David and all the house of Israel brought up the ark of the LORD with shouting, and with the sound of the trumpet."

So David is dancing. Not just calmly swaying back and forth with his hands slightly raise, but really dancing in the streets! He was dancing with all of his might. Let's picture that for a moment. He was unrestrained as he danced before the Lord and wasn't embarrassed about it because he was dancing for an audience of one.

Movement creates momentum. Dance, especially done in worship to God, helps create an atmosphere that welcomes breakthrough. Psalm 150:4 says, "Praise him with the timbrel and dance!" Dance creates movement in both the physical and the spiritual realms. Many of us may feel self-conscious about our dancing abilities, but I encourage you to try it! Get alone in your room if you have to and dance with all of your might before the Lord. The joy that it will bring to the heart of the Father is immeasurable.

Shouting

Shouting is another tool in our arsenal to build strength and wellness into our spirits. It seems odd to suggest shouting as a vehicle to build your spirit, yet the Word makes it clear the importance of this practice. The Psalms are filled with references to shouting. Psalm 5:11 says, "But let all those that put their trust in thee rejoice: let them ever shout for joy, because thou defends them: let them also that love thy name be joyful in thee."

We are called to shout with joy, which often happens during praise and worship. You'll notice some worship leaders will shout, "shout to God!" They are echoing Psalm 51 when it tells us to shout for joy to the Lord.

Victory comes in shouting and obedience to God's instruction. The story reads in Joshua 6:5, "And it shall come to pass, that when they make a long *blast* with the ram's horn, *and* when ye hear the sound of the trumpet, all the people shall shout with a great shout; and the wall of the city shall fall down flat, and the people shall ascend up every man straight before him." Then comes the good part in Joshua 6:16 where it says, "And it came to pass at the seventh time, when the priests blew with the trumpets, Joshua said unto the people, Shout; for the LORD hath given you the city." So they go and they shout! Joshua is saying that in order to get victory, sometimes you just have to shout! On the 7th day, they blasted their trumpets and lifted their voices with a shout and the wall fell down.

I have used this practice for myself many times. I have days where I'll notice that my attitude needs a bit of an adjustment. I love to walk and I live in the country, so I will often go on a walk and I'll try shouting when I can't get rid of something. I'll try praying, praising, and even being in the word, but sometimes all I need to do is just give a good shout! It helps release whatever is weighing heavy upon me.

Communion

Communion may be one of the most powerful spiritual acts there is. It is central to our spiritual strength. It is a commandment the Lord gave us in his last day. Why is it important? To answer that, let's first look at the account of the Last Supper. In 1 Corinthians 11 it says, "For I have received of the Lord that which also I delivered unto you, That the Lord Jesus the same night in which he was betrayed took bread: And when he had given thanks, he broke it, and said, Take, eat: this is my body, which is broken for you: this do in remembrance of me. After the same manner also he took the cup, after he had eaten, saying, this cup is the New Testament in my blood: this do you, as often as you drink it, in remembrance of me. For as often as you eat this bread, and drink this cup, you do show the Lord's death till he comes."

Here Paul is commanding us to do the sacraments for the purpose of reflecting on Christ, whose body was literally broken for us, and the blood of Christ that was shed for us.

Let's go back a bit and posture your heart towards what the word of God says. We are going to focus on the physical body of Christ first. In Isaiah 53:5 we read, "But he was wounded for our transgressions, he was bruised for our iniquities: the chastisement of our peace was upon him; and with his stripes we are healed." His body was cursed. It was cursed, as it says, like everyone who hangs on a tree. He was the curse of the law. When He sacrificed Himself, He allowed us to banish living from the curse and to live again from the blessings of God.

We ought to live in true and unbroken fellowship with the Lord, which is what He desires for us. We are called and empowered to take on His nature as revealed in 1 Peter, the divine nature of Jesus because in doing so, we are freed from the curse of the law.

The purpose of blood as the source for remission of sin is clear. In Hebrews 9:22 it says, "And almost all things are by the law purged with blood; and without shedding of blood is no remission." Jesus shed His blood for the forgiveness of our sins. It is clear that Jesus was the first sacrifice. God took Jesus and gave thanks for Jesus for what had to come to pass. He then broke Jesus, His body and His blood, so that we personally could have the forgiveness from sins and be free from the curse and have true, unbroken fellowship with Him. Then God gave Jesus back to us after His resurrection.

Jesus did all this because of his great love for us. He gives thanks for us in John 17. He breaks things off of us because we are in true unbroken fellowship and we must be transformed by the renewing of our mind. That freedom is so real that is hard to believe. A root study on the word "freedom" shows that it means "immunity." He gives us immunity. Our bodies can have immunity through the freedom He gives us in Him. So, that immunity comes from the freedom of being transformed in thought. He gives us back, personally restored to humanity so that we can now be a path of restoration for others back to the Father's love.

As a Doctor, the word immunity means everything. Communion represents such a high and holy thing, but sometimes it becomes rote and mundane when we don't internalize the truth and reality of all that it means. Do we allow the reality of Jesus' words "this is Jesus' body, broken for me, and this is Jesus blood shed for me" to carry their full weight? The point I want to make is that as we continue in unbroken fellowship, He can make all things new in you and He turns your bitter into sweet. When He breaks us, as gently as possible because He is kind, and as we are transformed by the renewing of our mind, that freedom and immunity comes back not only to every cell in our body, but to every thought in our life!

It's the purest form of love displayed by Christ. That he would sacrifice and break his body only to have it restored back. It's a pure metaphor of his intentions with us. He wants to break things off of us, transform us, and give us that unbroken fellowship with him.

Serving

"Rest and self-care are so important. When you take time to replenish your spirit, it allows you to serve others from the overflow. You cannot serve from an empty vessel. " Eleanor Brown.

The final sacred rhythm we will look at is serving. Serving is a beautiful thing when you see it for all that it is. It is a position where you learn to rule and enjoy leadership with a towel on your arm. Mark 10:45 says, "For even the Son of man came not to be served, but to serve, and to give his life a ransom for many."

Luke 22:26-27 says, "But you shall not be so: but he that is greatest among you, let him be as the younger; and he that is chief, as he that does serve. For who is greater, he that sits at table, or he that serves? Is not he that sits at table? But I am among you as he that serves." Jesus is questioning the traditional place of a leader, which shows us how important service is in His eyes.

When we follow Jesus, we have the privilege to serve and represent Him. As we serve Him, you and I get the privilege of standing in the presence of our heavenly Father. Eleanor Brown wrote, "Rest and self care are so important. When you take time to replenish your spirit, it allows you to serve others from the overflow. You cannot serve from an empty vessel. I have found that one of the things that will refresh me is to go and serve. "

I love the fact that I am a doctor because I get to serve patients every day. Every single day I get to serve somebody and I get to give life to that person. I have the honor of being able to speak life and love on them in the act of service. It is not only humbling, but it is exactly what Jesus did on earth.

There is nothing greater you can do for yourself than to go and serve someone who is in need. You will be more blessed than the one receiving your service! So I bless and pray for the desire in you to put a towel on your arm and rule with that towel.

Community

Surround yourself with people who make you hungry for life,
touch your heart and nourish your soul.

I want to highlight what I believe to be a final foundation piece to healing and wholeness and that is community. Biblically, we find strong support for that in countless Scriptures but let's take a look at the life of Moses and the Israelites that parallels the battle for health and wellness!

"Then Amalek [and his people] came and fought with Israel at Rephidim. So Moses said to Joshua, "Choose men for us and go out, fight against Amalek [and his people]. Tomorrow I will stand on the top of the hill with the staff of God in my hand." So Joshua did as Moses said, and fought with Amalek; and Moses, Aaron, and Hur went up to the hilltop. Now when Moses held up his hand, Israel prevailed, and when he lowered his hand [due to fatigue], Amalek prevailed. But Moses' hands were heavy and he grew tired. So they took a stone and put it under him, and he sat on it. Then Aaron and Hur held up his hands, one on one side and one on the other side; so it was that his hands were steady until the sun set.

So Joshua overwhelmed and defeated Amalek and his people with the edge of the sword. Then the Lord said to Moses, "Write this in the book as a memorial and recite it to Joshua, that I will utterly wipe out the memory of Amalek [and his people] from under heaven." And Moses built an altar and named it The Lord Is My Banner; saying, "The Lord has sworn [an oath]; the Lord will have war against [the people of] Amalek from generation to generation."

Let's start with some definitions. The Word is rich with multiple layers of meaning and revelation when we dig in to all that the Lord has packed in there for us to receive!

The word "Amelek" means sickness and disease, low points, and a valley. Contrast that to "Rephidim" which means rest! The battle for health is fought in rest! That battle is fought against Israel, which means "those who prevail with God." Not only does it refer to God being on your side, but it refers to community being along side you to help you win that battle. So, if we use the underlying meaning of just those few words, we can find some really significant revelation! I believe this story shows us that sickness and disease provoke a battle. When disease comes, it draws a fight against those who prevail with God in resting places. So when we are taking on the giant of illness, we need our identity to be solid in God and surround ourselves with a trusted and prepared group of people He prevails within.

Moving on, we see Moses whose name means "drawn out." He calls on Joshua whose name is "Jehovah is salvation." He tells him to put together a team to fight with Amalek. Moses goes to the top of the hill with the rod of God in his hand. To fight the battle, we see two things in operation: the one against whom the battle is drawn is the one who needs to get closest to God. Everyone has a role in the battle and each has to know not only their role, but also their position and responsibility. Moses' role is to take his position on the hill with the staff (a symbol of power) in his hand (God's will in action). He is not checked out. He is in battle-ready position in the high place of intimacy and connection and in the posture of worship to usher in the presence of the Lord. That place of connection and knowing brings strength and empowerment to overcome.

Allow me to digress for a moment. You and I are drawn out into a battle everyday. The question is whether we are coming from a place of rest, peace, and victory prior to beginning the war or are we beginning from a position of presumed defeat? How many times are we moved because we are given mans diagnosis for sickness and disease as though they are sovereign? God desires and invites YOU to a place of intimacy so you can hear his voice and move on what he is telling you.

The power of synergy in God is undisputed and clear in His word. If one can put a thousand to flight, two can put ten thousand to flight. In Deuteronomy 32:30 we read, "How could one chase a thousand and two put ten thousand to flight, unless their Rock had sold them and the Lord had given them up?"

That's the position of empowerment and strength we are offered in the battle of sickness and disease. That is what we are offered when we come into a place of intimacy with our team (community) in place.

Returning to Exodus 17:10, the battle begins and Moses ascends the hill with his companions. This is where "one accord," which is harmony and agreement, come in. Aaron and Hur were men he trusted implicitly and had history with who had his back. When we are in the midst of the battle, we need to surround ourselves with those with whom we have one mind and spirit with. We don't need solo heroes here. God calls us to the strength found in community. If we think about the power that comes with unity we would be more inspired to pursue it aggressively!

Reviewing the book of Acts, we find that the early church moved strongly in one accord and with power! In Acts 4:24 we read, "So when they heard that, they raised their voice to God with one accord and said: 'Lord, You are God, who made heaven and earth and the sea, and all that is in them.'"

God calls us into unified community because he never called us to conquer a battle alone. We need the strength of the Lord and each other to bring the synergy the word of God talks about! The kind of energy that makes 1+1=3. The interaction of elements, that's unified people together, and when combined produce a total effect that is greater than the sum of the individual elements, contributions, etc. Synergism which makes 1+1 =3.

By way of example, look at your iPhone or any electronic device you have in your possession. In and of itself, that iPhone creates isolation because it is a false sense of connection to the world. We can tend to think we are connected through calls, texts, and social media. Don't get me wrong, I love my iPhone and all that it does but texting is not true connection. Emails are fabulous, but still not a direct connection. Skyping is extraordinary and moving in the right direction, yet still limiting. Face to face interaction is truly when we connect. When we are face to face, in the presence of another, authenticity can happen. Authenticity is essential and vital to abundance and vibrancy in life! Be real and take a leap of faith and build community around you that can sustain you!

Interestingly, Moses did not go up to the hilltop alone. He was in community and relationship. He was not an island by himself but took with him people he trusted and were safe. He had a history with these men. These men were safe and had his back. You don't need to isolate and be heroic on your own to win. Regardless of the size of the battle we need each other and we need to willing as well to be vulnerable.

We live in a society that has created a high level of independence and an "I can do it myself" mentality. Satan wants you to live in isolation in the time of your greatest need. Yet you were born for relationship.

Returning to the passage, we see that when Moses held his arms up, the army prevailed and when he tired and dropped his arms, Amalek (disease) prevailed. To stay in that sustained place of connection and worship takes effort, intention and strength. When Moses acknowledged the heaviness of his hands, his companions entered. Aaron whose name means "lightbearer" and Hur who name means "noble" came alongside Moses. When Moses acknowledges his need and weakness, they put a stone (sacred object, foundation piece) under him so he could sit and find rest. They came alongside, much like the Holy Spirit, and held his arms up as well one on each side. Their support allowed his hands to be held up and steady (secure, freedom from danger or risk) until the sunset and in full view for all to see.

This speaks of the truth in Ecclesiastes where it says that a three-cord strand is not easily broken and highlights the power and strength in community. I think it is important to note that this battle is not stationary but rather it is active. We must move through the battle to victory.

In that victory, God calls for remembrance or a memorial. When there is victory, the Lord desires that we remember His faithfulness and His deeds in our lives. He instructs Moses to write this account in a book of remembrance and to speak it out as a testimony in Joshua's ears! The Lord declares that He will blot out the remembrance of Amalek (sickness and disease) under heaven! The testimony of Jesus is the Spirit of prophecy. Here, the testimony spoken is a precursor to all Jesus came to do: heal sickness and disease. Praise the Lord that there will be no warring in heaven where there is no sickness and disease. Praise the Lord for He has made a way here and now for sickness and disease to be overcome.

Moses' response to the victory is to build an altar. Moses built an altar (a place of sacrifice and remembrance) and called the name of it Jehovah Nissi: The Lord is my banner. Song of Songs says it most appropriately when it says, "His banner over me is love!" Love wins always and forever! His love for us wins an eternal reward and an abundant life from generation to generation.

The battle against the enemy will not end until we cross the divide, but we can count on his faithfulness to a thousand generations! Our path to wellness is not attained in isolation but in community! Find those people who make you hungry for life, touch your heart and nourish your soul!

You can be well!!! Go for it!!

Chapter 12

FREEDOM AND IMMUNITY

Now that we have explored what it looks like to rebuild, restore, and refresh our whole beings, let's look at what our ultimate goal is. It is freedom. What a powerful word. With many definitions and references throughout the Word, freedom is well worth the study and review.

Romans 6:11-18 says, "Let not sin therefore reign in your mortal body, that ye should obey it in the lusts thereof. Neither yield ye your members as instruments of unrighteousness unto sin: but yield yourselves unto God, as those that are alive from the dead, and your members as instruments of righteousness unto God. For sin shall not have dominion over you: for ye are not under the law, but under grace. What then shall we sin, because we are not under the law, but under grace? God forbid. Know ye not, that to whom ye yield yourselves servants to obey, his servants ye are to whom ye obey; whether of sin unto death, or of obedience unto righteousness? But God be thanked, that ye were the servants of sin, but ye have obeyed from the heart that form of doctrine, which was delivered you. Being then made free from sin, ye became the servants of righteousness."

What is true freedom? Since we are out from under the old tyranny, does that mean we can live any old way we want? Does that mean we can we do anything that comes to our mind? Hardly! You know well enough from your own experience that there are some acts of so-called freedom that actually destroy true freedom. Offer yourselves to sin and it is your last free act, but offer yourself to the ways of God and the freedom is unending. All of our lives, we have let sin tell us what to do. It's time for us to tell sin what to do. Thank God we have started listening to a new master whose commands set you free to live openly in His freedom.

As the renewed mind comes, it brings life to the reality of our opportunity to truly walk in freedom. If you've ever read Dr. Caroline Leaf's book, *Who Switched Off My Brain?*, it provides a lot of information about the physiology of thought and all the thoughts that you need to hold captive in order to capture the freedom for which you were intended. (She's brilliant and I highly recommend her book.)

Within 72 hours, once you switch off that rogue, lawless part of your brain and switch it on to the kingdom, you literally begin to start the new pathways of life and love in your brain. The old brain pathways become healed; the thorns of sin being removed and you lay down new pathways over the top of the old lies. The new ones bring fire, healing and life to your bones!

Interestingly enough, a synonym for freedom is "immunity. " I like to think of it as a diplomatic immunity, meaning that Satan can't touch you because you are bowed before the King of Kings and the Lord of Lords. Being renewed in the spirit of your mind brings immunity in your body.

The definition of immunity is "the ability of an organism to resist a particular infection or toxin, by the action of specific antibodies and sensitized white blood cells." In other words, immunity makes you stronger! Our immune system is housed in our bones! Deep within your body, inside your bones, your red and white blood cells are produced. The immunes system is strengthened when you choose the kingdom of heaven, day in and day out wen you are trusting in the Lord, with all your heart. It is seed upon seed and row upon row.

We spoke about when your resistance to sin increases, your God consciousness increases as well. You now have the resistance and freedom within your immune system so that you can rejoice and be glad because you are overcoming little by little, seed by seed, and row by row.

CONCLUSION

I have been practicing chiropractic care and walking people through these steps of healing for over twenty years. My husband and I have had the privilege of seeing close to ten thousand patients. Each and every patient comes with unique story. We've heard stories that range from heartbreak to tragedy, some of which have brought us to tears ourselves. However, we have learned that no matter the amount of pain that our patients have endured, God's grace and healing power is even greater! One of the greatest privileges God has given to me is to be able to witness His healing power in the lives of our patients.

My heart for writing this book is to be able to empower you for freedom! I believe in the power of the body, soul, and spirit that God has given us and when combined with the 3x3 grid, we are able to bring our healing to an entirely new level. I encourage you to be patient with yourself during this journey and invite the Holy Spirit to walk alongside you. Be open to His voice and allow yourself to be led according to His ways.

Beloved, God has not called you to live in captivity! He created you for freedom! My prayer is that when you begin implementing these tools that the fruit of your labor will become increasingly evident and sweet. I pray that you will have health to your flesh. Your flesh is blessing you back for choosing the sacred rhythms of your life. I release the blessing of health upon on as you begin to steward your precious body onto God…seed by seed and row by row.

You can be well.

Always,
Dr. Johnnett Thatcher